Measured and Drawn

While with slow eyes we these survey,
And on each pleasant footstep stay,
We opportunely may relate
The progress of this houses fate.

Andrew Marvell (1621–78), 'Upon Appleton House'

Measured and Drawn

*Techniques and practice for the metric survey of
historic buildings*

ENGLISH HERITAGE

Published by English Heritage, Kemble Drive, Swindon SN2 2GZ

Copyright © English Heritage 2003

Images (except as otherwise shown) © English Heritage
Application for the reproduction of images should be made to the National
Monuments Record. Every effort has been made to trace the copyright holders and
we apologise in advance for any unintentional omissions, which we would be
pleased to correct in any subsequent edition of this book.

First published December 2003

ISBN 1 873592 72 8

Product Code 50729

British Library Cataloguing in Publication Data
A CIP catalogue record for this book is available from the British Library.

Text by David Andrews, Bill Blake, Tom Cromwell and Richard Lea
Text compiled by Sarah Lunnon
Brought to publication by René Rodgers and Andrew McLaren, English Heritage
  Publishing
Edited by Susan Whimster
Designed by Michael McMann, mm Graphic Design

Printed by Arkle Print Ltd

Acknowledgements
Thanks are due to various people for their help in the production of this book:
Nick Beckett, English Heritage; Mark Bowden, English Heritage; Paul Byran,
English Heritage; Johnathon Clark, Field Archaeology Services, York; Mick
Clowes, English Heritage; Andy Crispe, English Heritage; David de Haan, Deputy
Director, Ironbridge Gorge Museum Trust; Donald Insall, Donald Insall and
Partners; and Kevin Leadingham, English Heritage. We also gratefully
acknowledge the following people and organisations who helped with the surveys
detailed in this book or gave permission to reproduce images or information:
Alexandra Palace (Fig 8); Andrew Townsend Architects; Steve Coll, Whitby Abbey
project (Fig 63); The Dean and Chapter of Peterborough Cathedral; John C
Goom, Kilpeck Church architect; Julian Limentani, Marshall Sisson Architects;
Richard Lithgow, Perry Lithgow Partnership; PCA Ltd; UK Robotic Ltd; and
Shelly White, Ironbridge Gorge Museum Trust.

Contents

1

Introduction

This document gives an introduction to the metric survey techniques currently available to conservation professionals and building archaeologists. Survey progresses from control to detail or 'from the whole to the part', so the description of survey techniques that follows progresses from control to detail, then to procurement, and concludes with case studies of metric surveys undertaken on historic buildings and structures.

The metric survey of our historic environment is a crucial part of our understanding. By mapping the historic estate it can be conserved, managed, enjoyed and its richness shared in confidence. An unfamiliar journey is not started without a map; the map is the key to the route and, at journey's end, it can be kept as a record that can inform others planning future journeys.

The English Heritage Metric Survey Team defines metric survey as 'the measurement and pictorial representation of land and buildings to a specified standard, supplying reliable and repeatable base data without specific thematic input'. This rather dry definition is an attempt to explain the process of measuring a building using known repeatable methods and then presenting the recorded information as a scaled drawing. This should be done with the minimum of thematic input, ie information from interpretative or analytical investigation, although it should be borne in mind that the interplay between thematic observation and the measurement process is often complex.

'The geometer, how excellent so ever he be, leaning only on to discourse of reason, without practice (yea and that sundry ways made) shall fall into manifold error, or inextricable Laberinthes.' So said Leonard and Thomas Digges in *Pantometria* (1571). Undertaking a successful metric survey requires a methodical systematic approach: employing the most sophisticated equipment will not prevent error without careful procedure.

The use of metric survey techniques to record historic buildings is particularly demanding. To this end considerable thought must be given to the purpose of a survey, its content, which techniques are most appropriate and how they can best be applied within any financial constraints. 'Fit for purpose' is a fundamental criterion for deciding what techniques should be deployed and how much detail is appropriate.

This publication is prepared in sequence with *The Presentation of Historic Building Survey in CAD* (English Heritage 1999) and *Metric Survey Specifications for English Heritage* (English Heritage 2000), as part of a series of technical guides for heritage recording.

1.1 Drawing conventions

A scaled line drawing is still seen as the conventional output of metric survey and it is useful to recognise that this product is based on a number of historically accepted conventions and concepts.

Traditionally, survey drawings are two-dimensional and the language or set of drawing conventions used to translate a three-dimensional structure into a two-dimensional image is the same for both designer and recorder. The drawn image is not a substitute for the real object but merely stands to communicate characteristics considered necessary for understanding the latter. The drawing process is accordingly highly selective in terms of both content and method. Fundamental to the conventions of metric survey are measurement and its associated geometrical concept of orthographic projection.

1.1.1 Orthographic projection

An orthographic projection is a drawing where the lines of projection are at right angles to the subject. This is more easily associated with elevation drawing than plans. For some buildings, the choice of viewpoint is obvious: the principal façade is paramount. But for others – especially those that have undergone alteration – it is often less clear.

1.1.2 Plan

The plan is such a commonplace element in our understanding of architecture that we forget how many assumptions underpin our use of this tool and even that it is a particularly interpretative form of sectional orthographic projection. Architectural plans do not simply describe the horizontal profile of a building at one specific level but also show us features within a single storey at several levels – such as doors and windows – and often incorporate ceiling and floor details. This can make for great complexity, but an effective drawing will clearly communicate this three-dimensional information. Deciding what to include in a plan is not necessarily a straightforward process, especially in buildings where there are multiple floor levels.

1.1.3 Section

This refers to a simple profile obtained by taking a cut-line through a building. It will show no detail in front of or behind the cut-line.

1.1.4 Sectional elevations

This term refers to drawings that describe detail in front of and behind the cut-line. Sectional elevations present the same range of problems encountered in plans with multiple floor levels. Deciding on an appropriate section line through a building is an essential step in the process of producing an intelligible drawing.

1.1.5 Scale

We do not draw buildings at a scale of 1:1, although in some instances we may draw details at this scale. The use of scale requires the simplification of detail, which in turn requires understanding, interpretation and analysis.

1.1.6 Detail

The drawing of details involves understanding which parts of the building require detail study and why. Constructional details often determine the form of a building detail, so special attention should be given to this factor in the drawing.

Detached details or fragments of buildings need to be understood in the context of the building in which they once stood. For this reason, it is important to select the appropriate viewpoints for drawing plans, elevations and sections. This is especially true for loose fragments of moulded stone, when it can prove difficult to determine the original orientation of a particular piece.

2
Control methods

Control measurements underpin the precision of the whole survey, so control data must be determined to a higher order of precision than that used for detail. Most control for building survey is undertaken using an electromagnetic distance measurer (EDM), although global positioning system (GPS) survey can supply Ordnance Survey national grid (OSNG) data to high orders of precision for larger sites and taped triangulation is still used, especially for internal building plans. EDM control methods use multiple observation to generate statistical precision by ameliorating instrument and observation error. Control methods are often specific to particular survey types, scale and speed of work. The methods of control described here are:

- triangulation
- simple linear control (baseline and end over end)
- traverse
- resection from three-dimensional detail points
- two-point intersection
- GPS
- wire-frame (graphical control) and existing computer-aided drafting (CAD) survey

2.1 Triangulation

All measured survey is based on the concept of baselines and the creation of triangles. The legs of a complex EDM traverse are essentially interlocking triangles and even satellite surveying by GPS is based on resolving triangles. The position of an object can be defined by the distances to it from the ends of a fixed baseline. Arcs of appropriate radius can be struck from each end of the baseline to plot the point where they intersect, forming a triangle with measured sides (Fig 1). In practice there are two possible solutions to such an equation, on either side of the baseline, but careful notation can eliminate any ambiguity.

2.1.1 Site grids

Site grids can be laid out through triangulation. When a grid is laid out with the use only of tapes, right-angle triangles are employed to set out the axes of the grid, using distances that fit a pattern of 3:4:5 or

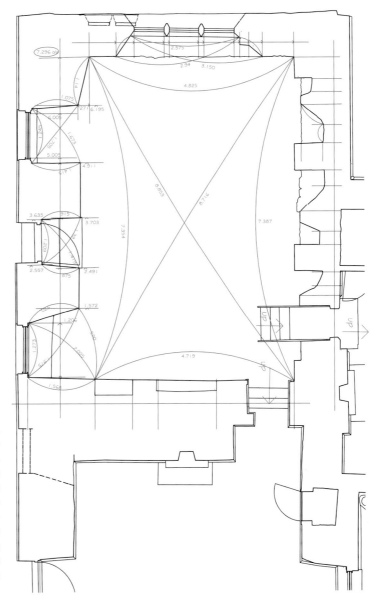

Figure 1
Simple triangulation used to produce a floor plan with baselines, radii and triangles as measurements, and 90-degree offsets shown and annotated.

3

other Pythagorean ratios. As with all survey control techniques rigorous measurement is required to gain adequate precision. The diagonals of the grid should be checked independently of the set-out process and the survey notes should state the method and likely precision of the control points (each point is rarely accurate to more than ±10mm in any direction as a result of the tape sagging and stretching). Unless the markers are levelled with a dumpy level or similar tool, their heights will be random and unknown; a separate marker to serve as a temporary benchmark (TBM) will then be required for independent height measurements.

2.1.2 Building plans

Building plans are commonly constructed by using taped diagonals and the side lengths of rooms matched together by the intersection of compass arcs (see Fig 1). Measuring plans by this method works well with other measured drawing techniques but can be unreliable when variations of height or complexity of shape require the fitting of many triangles. The plan of a large building comprising many rooms on several floors should not be attempted without a series of reliable control points linked together by a traverse (see Section 2.3). Triangulation or radial observation by reflectorless EDM (REDM) can be undertaken from known control points.

The plan of a small building can be measured up by triangulation very rapidly. A good sketch is vital to note the measurements and the preparation of such a sketch is a helpful procedure for understanding the building and which measurements are needed to plot it. The risks are that in imposing a triangulated geometry on the building distortions in the plan can be overlooked and that if adequate control is not in place the plan will not fit with adjoining buildings or rooms.

It is possible to use a hand-held 'distance only' EDM (such as Leica Geosystem Ltd's Disto™) rather than a tape. The advantage of this is that a single operator can use the devices but care should be taken as distances can be corrupted as a result of multiple measurement to internal corners and poor edge targeting. All hand-held EDMs should be checked carefully to find the effective performance range.

2.2 Simple linear control

2.2.1 Baseline

A drawing of a single wall or window may not need elaborate and costly control. A simple horizontal level line of known length and height can be used. This usually takes the form of two nails driven into the pointing at the same height with a string stretched between them and a measuring tape alongside with its end on one nail. This allows for offset measurements either above or below the level line. A similar process can be used vertically for recording Classical orders: for example, using a plumb bob to set up the vertical level and running a tape alongside it (see Fig 20).

A baseline is a reference marker for recording detail. On a large elevation a number of baselines may be used and struck when the detail is recorded. These baselines would be related back to a single datum line that would stay in place for the duration of the survey.

An alternative is to set up two stations on a floor, one at either end of the baseline, to act as a reference measurement to the subject being surveyed. Triangulation can be used to determine the position of the stations. Nails can be replaced by the use of self-adhesive targets and masking tape to avoid damage to historic fabric.

Whole drawings can be made from these kinds of simple control: for the drawing of a single elevation a plumb line and a datum line may be sufficient. Chalk is an easy and cheap material for marking plumb lines and datum lines. While the baseline method provides control for a single elevation, the elevation will not be related to any other survey of the site. To relate separate elevations together, at least three control points on each elevation will need to be surveyed on a common control using a theodolite or EDM to obtain three-dimensional coordinates.

2.2.2 End over end

It is possible to proceed through a small building by linking baselines together with EDM observation without the full rigour of a traverse (Fig 2). This is not without risk, as there is no check on the work unless a loop is closed. A station is occupied, a second is set out and the instrument and target positions are reversed; a new station is set out and so forth. The only check is the compared distance and height from one end of the set-out line to the other – hence the name 'end over end'. The procedure is similar to that of an open traverse and the data collected is of a lower order of precision compared to a closed traverse as formal adjustment or checks have not been applied (*see* Section 2.3).

2.3 Traverse

A traverse is a method of fixing the location of a series of points (known as 'stations') by means of distance and bearing measurements. The technique depends upon the precise measurement of distances and angles and the distribution of error by an applied adjustment. The development of robust angular measurement techniques in the 16th century, notably by Leonard and Thomas Digges (*Pantometria*, 1571), established the practice of measuring a precise framework of linked lines from which smaller measurements to detail could be made.

2.3.1 Traverse procedure

A traverse consists of a number of stations linked by lines known as 'legs'. To undertake a traverse at least three tripods are required. A theodolite is set up on a tripod at the second point and used to measure the angle between targets set up on tripods at the first and the third points. At the same time the EDM is used to measure the distances (ie the lengths of the legs) between the first and second and the second and third points. To proceed around the site the theodolite is moved to the third tripod and another tripod is set up on a fourth point. The tripod for the fourth point is usually that from the first point, which is no longer required. The angle between the second and fourth points is then measured along with the

Figure 2
Diagram of end-over-end control (also known as an open traverse).
i. A baseline is set out with the instrument at A; a station is put in at B.
ii. The instrument is then moved to B and a back-sight is taken to A.
iii. Next, a new station is put in at C.
iv. Lastly, a back-sight is taken to B.

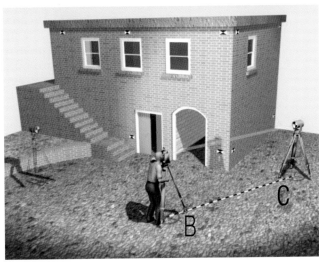

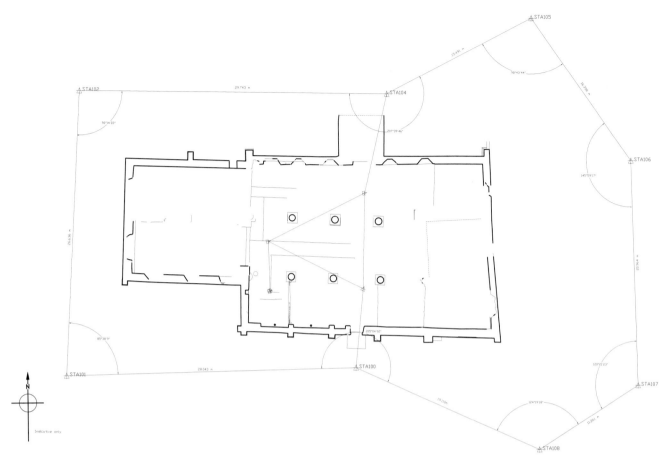

Figure 3
A closed traverse of the
church of St Giles, Oxford.

corresponding distances. The surveyor proceeds in this way until all the required ground is covered. If the traverse returns to its starting point it is called a 'closed traverse' (Fig 3), if not it is known as an 'open traverse'. Traverses can be used to link two points of known value and these are called 'link traverses'. Traverses are useful because they generate control points of a high order of precision that enables detail mapping to fit to a wider scheme when needed.

2.3.2 Equipment for EDM traversing

A typical traversing set will comprise:

● three tripods with adjustable legs
● three tribrachs, interchangeable and fitted with optical or laser plummets
● two prism reflectors and carriers
● one EDM/theodolite instrument
● one data recorder/logger.

The measurement axes of the instrument and prisms must occupy the same height above the tribrach, thus ensuring a common height of collimation for both target and instrument when set up over the same tribrach. Using equipment from the same manufacturer can ensure this uniformity, but unfamiliar equipment should be checked.

2.3.3 Observation procedure

The precision of a traverse depends on the reliability of instrument observations. By using a repeated observation technique a statistical measurement of the precision of the network can be used to balance, reduce and distribute proportionally errors in the traverse. Much of the calculation involved in obtaining observation averages and error distribution can be undertaken by metric survey software and some data loggers can undertake the process on site.

2.4 Resection from three-dimensional detail points

Resection is a useful technique in circumstances where setting out station positions obscures sight lines – for example, on staircases, in roof spaces and in cellars (Fig 4). A set of reference marks can be placed on a wall in the area to be surveyed and observed from the current instrument position. These can then be used to determine a new station position. If an REDM is used, quite effective control can be applied without the use of a second tripod.

Resections work well provided that:

- targets are carefully chosen for reflectance
- angles are well conditioned
- reference positions are clearly marked
- obliqueness in the vertical axis is avoided.

2.5 Two-point intersection

Two point intersection is a technique for obtaining the coordinates of three-dimensional points to a high order of precision using a theodolite and EDM. The points must be easily identifiable as they are observed from two stations. A common use of intersection is for photogrammetric control where targets are usually attached to the subject.

Two stations are set up on a baseline parallel to the subject, usually as part of a traverse, in order to link the control points to a site grid. The distance between the two stations is measured in both directions to provide an average reading. Horizontal and vertical angles are measured to each of the targets from both of the stations and both faces are used in order to improve accuracy. For observing extreme vertical angles a right-angle eyepiece will be required.

The angles and the distance between the two stations are used to calculate distances from the stations to the control points. These can then be used to produce coordinate values. The procedure actually produces two height values, so these are averaged. The difference between the two heights can be used as an indication of accuracy. In most cases it should be possible to achieve a height difference of 1 to 2mm or better (Fig 5).

2.6 GPS

The use of GPS equipment allows for the rapid creation of survey stations linked to the OSNG in open fields without the need for lengthy traverses from Ordnance Survey (OS) control points. The limitations are the precision, which is sufficient for most landscape survey but is still not as accurate as a good instrument traverse, and the need to have a clear view of the sky in order to receive satellite signals. GPS will not work

indoors, under tree cover, or near the sides of buildings. GPS cannot apply control points directly to an elevation, so it must be supplemented by traditional EDM equipment for building survey.

Collecting reliable data requires both survey skill and specialist training. The technical nature of GPS, the equipment required and its limitations restrict its use for historic building survey to the introduction of control to large sites and linking large groups of buildings together.

2.6.1 Scale factors

Where the site covers a large area or is to be recorded as part of a wider area, project coordinate values need to respect the projection used to map the wider area. The OSNG uses a transverse mercator projection to transfer the curvature of the earth and the effects of variation in height on to a two-dimensional curved plane. A scale factor is adopted to correct directly observed measurements for the projection used. This can be applied at the point of capture or as a post-process adjustment. Care must be taken in applying the correct local scale factor as this will vary with longitude.

If a scale factor is to be applied it is important to ensure that all members of the recording team are aware of it so that the mismatch between adjusted and unadjusted work can be anticipated. Control points derived from GPS survey should be supplied with a statement of the projection used and the local scale factor.

2.7 Wire-frame (graphical control) and existing CAD survey

CAD is the optimum assembly platform for three-dimensional data sets. The precision of the CAD environment matches that of the survey data and supplies the three-dimensional tools required for data completion.

The integration of differing data types in CAD requires a common control system and scale factor to be employed. More commonly, where a survey already exists in a CAD format, it can be used as the basis for later survey work. The 'wire-frame' outline from photogrammetry can be used to identify control points for resection and in hand survey can provide a framework for detail infill.

Figure 4

A diagram showing the angles and distances measured at resection.

i. From the current station two targets are marked on a wall and values obtained for their positions.

ii. The instrument is then moved and set up where the new station is required. From the new station the angles and distance are measured to the first target.

iii. Then to the second.

iv. The resolution of the point observation can then be used to determine the position of the new station and so allow detail capture.

Figure 5

Two-point intersection is used for obtaining the coordinates of three-dimensional points to a high order of precision, in order to control targets or detail points on stereo-photographs. The angles α, α' and β' plus the distance D allow the calculations D' and D" and thus the coordinates of the target.

In this way an outline plot from photogrammetry or rapid REDM survey can be enhanced with detail that might only be visible from scaffolding or after the removal of an obstruction that existed at the time of the first survey. Outline or wireframe CAD data of buildings can also be used to control standard photographs, as described in Section 3.2.2.

2.7.1 CAD modelling

CAD models of three-dimensional structures can be built from the three-dimensional wire-frame data generated by an EDM or photogrammetry. Good quality control is vital for the fitting together of three-dimensional components and this can only be achieved by a rigorous survey method. Terrain models can work well with tolerances in the 1:100 to 1:1000 range but for structures such as buildings and bridges at scales of 1:50 or 1:20, the demands on the control system can push positional precision to sub-millimetre levels. If the model is to achieve integrity equivalent to a 1:50 scale, objects will need to be positioned to ±5mm in X,Y and Z across the whole subject. A set of high-order control stations should be set up so that local control can be easily carried forward for close-range EDM work (*see* Section 5.4).

2.8 Appropriate control

Control will underpin the entire building survey and its precision and accuracy will directly affect the quality of detail data recorded. When a survey is planned the control requirement for the subject should be assessed and the surveyor briefed accordingly. Selection of the appropriate control technique is a matter of matching the demands of the subject, the required scale and the future use of the survey. If survey is to be carried out on a site by different teams at different times the control must be safeguarded accordingly.

Prior to putting control on to any site it is essential to undertake a site reconnaissance. The importance of this cannot be overstated. It will enable the surveyor not only to obtain an overview of the entire job but also to observe where problems are likely to occur and to take steps to overcome them.

3
Metric survey techniques

Metric survey can usefully be divided into two separate sections, referred to here as image-based and non-image-based survey.

Image-based survey techniques form part of a range of land-survey techniques that have been developed to record historic buildings and their environment. The data source for image-based survey is the visual image, in either a photographic or digital-based format, together with an element of scale. These are used to generate the required detail and are presented in either a line drawing or scaled-image format.

Where there is a clear open view of a large subject, such as an exterior wall, the application of image-based survey provides economical cover through mass-data capture. Image-based survey, in particular the use of controlled stereo-pairs, provides a flexibility of output. Products that can be generated are: a record photograph, a line drawing, a three-dimensional digital terrain model (DTM), an orthophotograph and perspective views. The image (photograph) will also provide a record of time and place, which can become a useful archive document in its own right.

Non-image-based survey is also referred to as architectural survey. The data sources for an architectural survey can include hand measurements, instrument measurements, information from image-based survey (eg do-it-yourself (DIY) controlled rectified photography or photogrammetry), and laser scanning. The integration of such disparate data sources is most commonly undertaken using CAD.

Traditionally, the product of a measured survey is a scaled line drawing supplied as a plan, section, elevation or sectional elevation. Using CAD as the assembly platform for data sets, however, has seen the development of three-dimensional digital models as products of metric survey.

The integrated use of survey techniques is often required for complete cover of a monument and common control is fundamental to its achievement. Where survey techniques are to be procured thought must be given to how the techniques will work together; this becomes more important where more than one contractor is involved and the survey is conducted over an extended period of time. Documentation and survey-station witness diagrams are essential.

3.1 Image-based survey techniques

The term 'image-based survey' is used to describe rectified photography, photogrammetry and orthophotography. The first uses a single image while photogrammetry and orthophotography require stereo-photography. Everything that can be seen by the camera is recorded and with orthophotography and rectified photography this detail is carried through to the final product. The end result of photogrammetry is usually a line drawing produced by operator selection, but the photography is always available for reference. Where there are no obvious lines to collect, photogrammetry can be used to map a surface to produce a DTM.

3.1.1 Rectified photography

Rectified photography is a relatively quick and simple survey method useful in circumstances where the subject is flat and contains a large amount of textural detail. However, the technique must be used with caution. A standard photograph of, for example, a wall cannot usually be used to scale off accurate dimensions because of errors caused by one or more of the following:

- the camera lens was not completely distortion free. This is usually the case with 35mm cameras, especially those with wide-angle lenses
- the façade of the wall is not completely flat so parts of the wall nearer the camera appear to be larger than those further away
- the photograph was not taken with the negative plane of the camera completely parallel to the façade of the wall so the scale varies across the image (Fig 6).

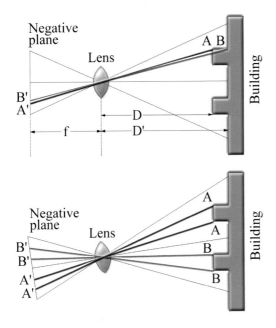

To rectify means to correct, adjust or redress an error. In the term 'rectified photography' the correction applies to errors in the scale and position of objects in a photograph.

Error reduction

Although we use the term 'rectified photography' the usual aim is to minimise error while taking the photography and to make only minor adjustments by rectification. Error as a result of lens distortion is reduced by using a high-quality large-format (5in. × 4in.) camera and taking care to ensure that the camera is parallel to the façade will lessen the risk of varying scale. A monorail camera is ideal because the rising front and other movements can be used to avoid tilting the camera.

If a wall is made up of a number of distinct planes it is possible either to scale the same photograph several times or to take separate photographs for each plane. Where a wall is undulating or highly detailed, rectified photography is not suitable.

Scale and control

To allow the rectified photograph to be printed to a specific scale a method of scaling must be used. This can take the form of a simple scale bar or targets can be attached to the façade. The distances between the targets can be found with a tape measure or their positions can be coordinated using a theodolite.

Photographic negatives can be printed using darkroom methods or scanned for use with digital rectification software. Where darkroom methods are employed the enlarger head will be raised or lowered until the required scale is achieved by matching the image against a scale rule or a plot of the targets. Slanting the baseboard can compensate for minor tilts. If digital methods are employed, four coordinated targets per image are usually required although some systems can make use of assumed horizontals and verticals (Fig 7). Examples of digital rectification packages currently available include Archis from Galileo Siscam and MSR from Rolleimetric. There is also a rectification facility within ERDAS Imagine.

Once the image has been rectified it can either be printed directly at the required scale or imported into a CAD package, where the image data can be combined with vector data to produce a composite product. With most digital rectification packages it is possible to mosaic a number of photographs together. This facility is useful for subjects such as tiled floors, where it is impossible to cover the whole subject with one camera shot (Fig 8).

DIY rectified photography

It is possible for the non-professional surveyor to undertake rectified photography projects successfully. Small areas can be covered using a standard 35mm camera, although the larger the format and the better the quality of the camera, the better the results will be. It should also be remembered that the wider the angle of the lens the greater the lens distortion will be, particularly at the corners of the format. As well as the camera, a tripod, a hot shoe spirit bubble and a 1m-long spirit level will be required.

Figure 6
A standard photograph can contain errors of scale as a result of camera tilt and the changing depth of the subject.

Figure 7
The digital rectification process. The original photograph of a wall painting at Westminster Abbey, right, was scanned and then rectified using the Archis rectification process, producing the image on the left.

Figure 8
An example of a rectified
mosaic. Twelve
photographs were used in
the construction of this
mosaic image of a ceiling at
Alexandra Palace.

The camera is mounted on the tripod and levelled using the hot shoe bubble. This ensures that the vertical axis of the negative plane is vertical and thus parallel to the façade (assuming the façade is vertical). To set the horizontal axis of the negative plane parallel, the 1m spirit level is positioned level and parallel to the façade. The camera is then rotated from side to side until the spirit level appears to be parallel with the base of the view-finder window or, if a 5in. × 4in. camera is being used, the ground-glass back. For this method to work the spirit level must appear close to the bottom or top of the format. Where more than one photograph is required to cover a façade it will usually be necessary to use coordinated control targets for scaling rather than just a scale bar. This will help maintain overall accuracy as the distance from the first photograph to the last will be known.

Even without access to a darkroom or rectification software it is still possible to employ rectified photography. Normal machine prints of photographs taken in the manner described above can be used with a digitising tablet to produce line drawings in CAD. The tablet will have to be calibrated using coordinate values for targets appearing in the photographs, or will need a scale bar. Images from digital cameras or scanned negatives can be inserted into drawings in recent CAD packages (eg AutoCAD R14 and later) and rotated to fit detail or control points. Detail can then be digitised on screen or the image can be used as part of the drawing in its own right.

To understand the scope and limitations of the technique practitioners with little or no previous experience may require field and office practice. The DIY rectified photographer will also benefit from hands-on knowledge of CAD, access to good-quality three-dimensional control and a methodical and systematic approach to undertaking survey.

3.1.2 Photogrammetry

Where a line drawing of a large area such as a whole building façade is required, photogrammetry is the most economical survey method available and also produces the best overall accuracy. It is most effective when applied to subjects where line detail is easily identified, such as an ashlar wall. Since the final product is a CAD drawing it can easily be edited by the end-user.

Photogrammetry is the technique of making precise measurements and drawings from stereo-photographs. Stereo-photographs are overlapping photographs of the same subject taken from slightly different positions, commonly known as stereo-pairs (Figs 9 and 10).

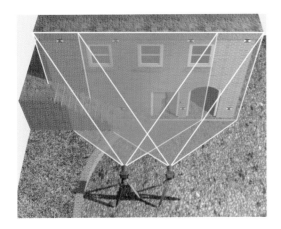

A standard photograph cannot be used for measurement because inherent within it are the following errors: first, a photograph is a perspective projection, which means that if the subject has any depth or if the camera is tilted relative to the façade there will be scale or displacement errors; secondly, standard cameras also exhibit lens and film distortion. The photogrammetric process uses specially made 'metric' cameras that have little or no lens distortion and contain a mechanism for ensuring film flatness. They also have small reference points in the negative plane, known as 'fiducial marks', which appear in the image and allow for subsequent correction of any film distortion that may occur (*see* Fig 10). The cameras are calibrated so that the focal length and any lens distortion are precisely known.

In order to eliminate the problems caused by perspective projection, two overlapping photographs – known as a 'stereo-pair' – are acquired. The greater the distance from the subject the larger the area covered in the photographs. However, the area covered must be balanced against the need for resolution of detail in the photograph. To maintain accuracy the scale of the image on the negative must be within certain constraints, so it is often necessary to acquire a number of stereo-pairs to cover one subject such as a building façade.

The stereo-pairs are set up in a stereo-plotter, which allows the photographs to be viewed as a three-dimensional stereo-model. Stereo-plotters are either computer-controlled optical mechanical systems that use transparencies, or digital systems that use scanned photographs. The stereo-model is an orthographic projection, which means that it is not subject to errors caused by the relief of the subject. The two photographs are adjusted with regard to each other in order to eliminate errors resulting from different tilts of the camera.

In order to make precise measurements from the stereo-model and to relate it to any other models, control points with three-dimensional coordinate values are employed. These usually take the form of small plastic targets attached to the subject before the photographs are taken. Alternatively, existing points of detail may be used. The targets

Figure 9
Diagram showing the camera set-up required for acquiring a stereo-pair.

Figure 10
Stereo-pair of Whitby Abbey. Eight stereo-pairs were required to provide complete cover of the east face of Whitby Abbey church. The camera used for this stereo-pair was a UMK 5in. × 4in. format with 300mm lens. The red notation on the stereo-pair marks the detail points used for control. Note the fiducial marks on the border of the image: here they take the form of small circles, although the type of mark depends on the camera.

*Figure 11 (above, left)
A photogrammetric
operator producing a CAD
drawing from a stereo-pair
using a Leica SD2000
analytical plotter.*

*Figure 12 (above, right)
Part of the photogrammetric
drawing of the east face of
Whitby Abbey church,
plotted from a CAD file.*

are coordinated using a theodolite and EDM. The coordinates will generally be on a site grid so that different façades can be related to one another.

Once the stereo-model has been set up, a skilled operator records the detail with a measuring mark (Fig 11). In order to produce an accurate drawing the operator must control the floating mark so that it appears to rest on the detail that is being traced round. Coordinates are fed from the

stereo-plotter into a CAD system to form the drawing (Fig 12). The content of the drawing will depend on the detail visible in the photographs and the operator's interpretation of the detail. Where, for example, a window reveal is not visible in both photographs it will not be possible to record any detail. Surfaces of elevations or landscape can be mapped by recording three-dimensional points on a grid to produce a DTM (Fig 13). With a digital photogrammetric system it is

*Figure 13
Screen shot of a DTM
produced from a stereo-
pair. This figure forms part
of a medieval tympanum
that has subsequently been
reused in a folly at
Shobdon Arches,
Herefordshire.*

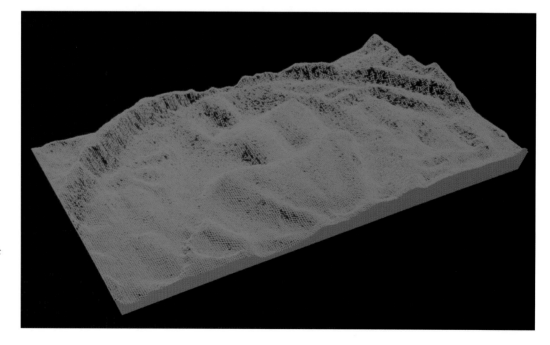

possible automatically to produce a DTM that can then be used either in its own right or to generate an orthophotograph.

3.1.3 Orthophotography

An orthophotograph is a photograph that has been corrected for any errors arising out of the relief of the subject or tilts of the camera relative to the façade, ie there is no variation in scale across the image (Figs 14 and 15). Orthophotographs are useful when an image-based product is required but the subject is too three-dimensional for rectified photography to be applied.

Orthophotographs are a product of digital photogrammetry and the wider use of digital photogrammetry has contributed to their growing popularity. Using the digital photogrammetric process it is possible to produce a DTM that is an accurate representation of the surface of the land or elevation of a building (*see* Fig 13). The DTM can then be used to adjust the scale of an image pixel by pixel and thus convert a photograph with perspective projection to one with an orthographic projection – an orthophotograph. The stereo-photography for

an orthophotograph of a building must be taken as square on to the façade as possible so as to minimise any gaps in the image that might occur (eg where a cornice obscures the detail above it).

Once the orthphotograph has been produced it can be printed out at the required scale or imported into a CAD package. Within the CAD package it can be combined with line data from conventional photogrammetry to produce a composite product. It should be remembered that an orthophotograph is normally a two-dimensional product and so will contain no information about depth or the Z-coordinate. It is possible, however, to drape the orthophotographic image over the DTM using a three-dimensional modelling or visualisation package (*see* Section 5.6).

3.1.4 Application of image-based survey techniques

The decision as to whether an image-based or other survey technique is the most appropriate type of survey for a particular subject is influenced by three factors.

Figure 14 (above, left)
A standard photograph of the south doorway of Kilpeck church, showing scale distortion.

Figure 15 (above, right)
An orthophotograph of the south doorway of Kilpeck church. The orthoprojection allows the entire doorway to be viewed at the same scale. (Compare this with Fig 14.) Topographic detail can be combined with orthophotographs if required, with the line drawing appearing on top of the photographic image (see Fig 65).

Fitness for purpose

The obvious difference between photogrammetry and orthophotography or rectified photography is that the former results in a line drawing while the latter two produce an image. In many cases a line drawing is preferred because a certain amount of interpretation is performed while the drawing is made. For example, a line drawing of a coursed-rubble façade will often accentuate the building phases, thus aiding archaeological understanding. In other cases an image-based product will be required because the textural detail of the subject would not be adequately portrayed by a line drawing (eg the colours of different lithologies or the intricate detail of wall paintings).

Technical considerations

The successful application of rectified photography needs careful consideration. It can be used to produce an accurate survey of walls, floors and ceilings, but only if the subject is flat. Where the subject is three-dimensional because of openings, changes in building phase and fabric loss, or is of undulating structure (eg a historic floor), another method must be employed. The use of stereo-pairs allows photogrammetry and orthophotography to be applied to a three-dimensional subject. The end-product of orthophotography is a two-dimensional image, unlike the three-dimensional digital photogrammetric drawing product, so consideration has to be given to whether the survey will be analysed in three dimensions.

Digital and analytical photogrammetric systems now enable a line drawing to be produced from very heavily tilted photographs. Nevertheless, rectified photography still needs to be taken as near parallel to the subject as possible. Digital rectification software can cope with quite large tilts but at the expense of image quality. This is because, in effect, the area of the subject furthest from the camera will have been photographed at a smaller scale and thus each pixel in the digital image will cover a larger area. Again, orthophotography can cope with the same tilts as conventional photogrammetry but where detail is hidden from the camera the surrounding pixels will be stretched to fill in the gaps, with messy results.

Cost

Commercially procured orthophotography is usually twice the price of rectified photography and photogrammetry is three times

the cost, so it is important to decide what survey product is really needed. If the survey is required as a pre-intervention or ante-disaster record then a photogrammetry fieldwork package may be all that is necessary. This would result in a considerable cost saving and would also allow the production of drawings at a later date. If high degrees of accuracy are not necessary then rectified photography can be used on a slightly three-dimensional subject and the inherent errors accepted as the price for cost saving.

If a cheap but inappropriate survey method is employed, the danger is that any cost savings will be lost owing to the miscalculation of quantities or as a result of extra staff time having to be spent in hand-correcting the survey.

3.2 Non-image-based survey techniques

These types of survey involve contact with the building at a level not often achieved with image-based techniques. Most non-image-based survey techniques are particularly suited to confined spaces or areas of complex detail where more remote methods cannot reasonably be deployed. The level of intimacy gained allows for the sensitive presentation of such structures. Laser scanning, unlike other non-image-based survey techniques, enables the surveyor to undertake mass-data capture of a building (with one type of laser) or small areas of detail (with a different type of laser). Most non-image-based devices only allow small areas to be recorded at any time.

3.2.1 Surveying with EDM

Rapid and precise measurement using EDM gives a reliable framework to survey work of all kinds, but especially in close-range work (5m to 100m). Precision is dependent on the density of recorded points and the method used. EDM is becoming more widespread and its application to close-range detail work is now possible with reliable REDM and real-time links to CAD from software such as TheoLT (LatimerCAD). The guidance on technique offered here should be used in conjunction with that available from the manufacturers and suppliers of the hardware and software involved. Useful references and further reading can be found in Appendix 3.

EDM is a line-of-sight measurement method that involves measuring to a given target, usually a retro-reflective prism. Data is recorded by measuring the distance and the horizontal and vertical angles to the reflector, giving a precise reading (typically 2.0mm at a range of 500m). Using an EDM is rapid and precise, but requires the surveyor to select the data to be recorded in the field. It is not a mass-data capture method like photogrammetry or laser scanning.

There are various distance-only EDM devices (eg Disto™) and these can be considered as tools for hand measurement unless they are being used as real-time CAD sensors.

Operators of EDM instruments should be familiar with common survey practice so that they can set up over a point and understand:

- the expected performance of angular and distance measurement
- the importance of level and plumb axes for measurement
- calibration and verification of instrument error
- the correct sequence of measurement to ensure appropriate precision for both control and detail work
- the appropriate point density for the desired drawing quality at a given scale.

REDM

REDM units are available that are ideal for recording work on buildings. An REDM uses the same principle as a reflector-based EDM, but relies on reading the return signal from the target rather than from a prism reflector (Fig 16). Typically, REDM units have a useful range of 5m to 200m, with a reduced precision compared to EDM (±3mm at 30m range is standard). An REDM has two principal benefits over an EDM:

- speed of targeting
- access to remote targets.

An REDM can be operated as a one-person system given that there is no need for someone to place a prism reflector at the target. In practice, however, two people are often required, as subjects usually require a mix of targeting methods to provide complete coverage.

Data captured using an REDM needs careful monitoring so that spurious points are not recorded. There are three variables that affect the precision of reflectorless measurement:

- range: the return signal is diminished and the contact area of the measuring beam is increased with long-range observations
- obliqueness: the ambiguity over the targeted point increases with the obliqueness of the observation and distances will be corrupted
- reflectance: the reflective quality and surface texture of the target will affect the ability to measure distances.

Target and station selections are determined by these variables: the need for stations to be close to the subject and the necessity for operators to avoid targeting to edges with an oblique aspect to the instrument.

Four simple steps will help get the best from reflectorless measurement:

- the use of real-time CAD capture (such as TheoLT) to monitor the recorded points and lines to allow verification of the measurement results (*see* Fig 16)
- using a card target for edges to improve precision when measuring to edges, as the card will resolve split-beam ambiguities (Fig 17)

Figure 16
An REDM being used on site. The red dot is used as a pointer because the laser performing the measurement is not visible. A field computer is being used to capture the CAD survey data in real time.

- keeping the ranges as short as possible
- using overlap observations from one instrument set-up to the next as a check.

Data logging

Data logging falls into the following two groups:

- post-process data logging is generally used for DTMs and control work at scales between 1:500 and 1:2500. If rapid capture and field-equipment survival are more important than detailed verification, a post-process approach will give the benefit of robust field kit and speed of capture
- real-time CAD is a method of digitising three-dimensional data from the instrument directly into a CAD environment. The use of real-time CAD capture is of great benefit for large-scale close-range work, such as the recording of detail for historic building survey. When used with reflectorless instruments surveyors can edit and complete data in CAD at the point of capture. Close-range reflectorless work, such as internal building survey, is best recorded by real-time CAD.

Data-recording devices differ for post-process or real-time CAD. Real-time data capture requires the use of a field computer to plot the observations in their correct positions in CAD. A laptop computer can be used, but it will be exposed to site conditions. Post-process loggers are tough and require low power, but their application is limited to coding the observation string as a means of data separation and definition.

To get the most out of real-time CAD a field computer is required. The best models are those that use a pen interface and have daylight-readable screens. These are more expensive than a standard laptop computer and will need either external power from spare batteries or power on site. Protection from the weather is essential and all cables will need to be of a robust quality. Ruggedised computers vary widely in specification and performance, so it is important to check details such as data exchange, power supply and screen performance carefully before choosing a field unit. Working with a computer in the field can be demanding on both the user and the hardware: a safe mounting bracket is a wise investment as it will guard the machine from costly damage and will improve the work environment for the surveyor (*see* Fig 16).

An EDM can be used directly with CAD via an interface such as TheoLT, making it possible for survey data to be recorded in real-time directly into CAD. The method requires a computer to run CAD on site, an EDM set-up and the TheoLT software. The surveyor can then draw detail using the EDM to position points and lines in the three-dimensional CAD drawing (Fig 18; *see also* Fig 16).

Being able to view while on site the plotted result of REDM observations as they are made makes it possible for the surveyor to check on the integrity of data collected and to assess what distance observations are still required. The view can be in plan, elevation, isometric or any suitable combination that enables the three-dimensional integrity of the work to be monitored as the data is collected. Because the surveyor is collecting data in CAD, use of standard CAD tools is possible giving the work a rapid field to CAD path. The product is a three-dimensional wire-frame that can be used as an outline for the control of hand survey, photography or a complete drawing.

Hand-held distance-only EDM devices (such as Disto™) can be used as real-time CAD sensors. Two-dimensional geometry can be built up by plotting the intersection of arcs, offsetting and copying lines by distance input from the Disto™ using TheoLT to interface to AutoCAD.

When CAD data for site work is prepared, the field CAD work needs to be separated from other data sources. This can be done by using the layer facilities in CAD, so that the fitting of blocks is possible if there is a mismatch between the site work and any earlier work. Setting up the required views for the job before the site work begins is to be recommended, since much time can be lost trying to navigate around a large

Figure 18
A sectional elevation
prepared for fieldwork.
Note the use of viewports
enabling the data to be
viewed from different
angles. This facility, used
with rigorous layer
management, makes it
possible to identify and
understand the three-
dimensional building data
being recorded, which
means that informed
decisions can be made
about any further data
capture required on site.

cumbersome drawing – it is better to use small drawing files on site (*see* Fig 18).

Drawing in CAD is a slow process but it can be rewarding. Use of the following can help speed up the process and simplify data management:

- if the subject permits offsetting lines for window details and closing shapes, then using fillet, extend and trim can be effective but a balance must be made with photographing or sketching detail for later off-site CAD work
- setting up views of sectional elevations from a wire-frame can help in the selection of detail to be included and is essential in elevation work
- data can be separated and edited by layer for line weight and type rather than by the alternative coding method
- full-size details can be worked up in CAD away from the site and then fitted to precise three-dimensional positions (the wire-frame) captured from the on-site EDM.

3.2.2 Using a CAD wire-frame

Photography

Tracing detail from standard photographs is unreliable as the photographs will not be true to scale and will contain perspective distortion. If an EDM trace is made of the subject's key features the wire-frame can be used in CAD to resize the scanned image to fit. REDM is well suited to this work as the number of observations can be increased from single points to lines, drawing outline detail in real-time using TheoLT (Fig 19).

When a wire-frame is used to trace detail from photography, the procedure is as follows:

- use field CAD to help match the wire-frame to the image areas and monitor the former's integrity
- ensure that all planes of the subject are adequately covered by the wire-frame
- check overlapping data from adjacent images
- test the image scale against the wire-frame to check for obliqueness
- keep the range between the instrument and subject as short as possible
- take photography as square in as possible and overlap the images.

The effectiveness of using photography in this way is limited to the ability to control the image area: if a large area across several images is to be mapped, serious consideration should be given to alternative techniques such as photogrammetry or orthophotography.

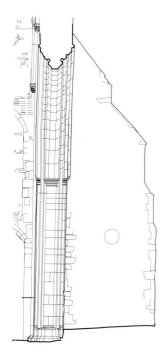

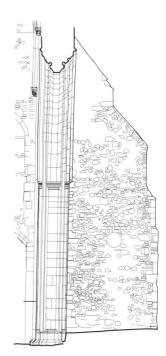

Figure 19

Using an REDM and a real-time CAD trace to control survey detail from a photograph.

Left: The REDM trace, the wire-frame, collected to match the photograph.

Centre: A scanned photograph of the detail area: note the effect of camera tilt on the dressed quoins.

Right: Detail of the rubble infill has been traced off the scanned photograph in CAD. The scale correction was applied in CAD using a three-dimensional rotation of the image to fit the wire-frame.

Measured drawing

Measured drawing can be controlled in much the same way as photography. The drawings should be annotated to include the EDM-observed outline (usually by marking the lines in red on the drawing) so that the plot can be fitted to the control when the drawing is being constructed in CAD.

Because EDM requires a high order of target selection it is rarely (with the notable exception of small-site topographic surveys) the sole method of data collection; it is far more common to combine data from EDM with drawings prepared by hand measurement or derived from photography.

3.2.3 Hand survey

The term 'hand survey' can refer to any record made of a site by hand, with measurement or not. It encompasses a rough sketch of a site made during reconnaissance, construction diagrams and measured drawings of architectural forms. Image-based and other remote-survey methods, when used appropriately, provide fast and economic means of recording historic structures, but these techniques are distant or isolated from the historic structure. Hand survey requires an intimate contact with the building, enabling an understanding of the structure and attention to detail not available from the other techniques. The use of hand-survey techniques also enables the production of a precise, detailed survey drawing using minimal survey equipment. Hand survey is more reliant on the observational skills, subjective judgements and knowledge of the practitioner undertaking the survey than other survey techniques.

Measured drawing

This term refers to the techniques used to measure directly the fabric of part or all of a building and then to record this information by hand on paper or into a hand-held computer. Measured survey can be conducted as a stand-alone recording method. More often it is employed in areas where

- access is limited for survey instruments
- there is a specific requirement to record complex architectural detail not suited to image-based or remote techniques
- the infill and enhancement of drawings produced by image-based methods is required. In this way, the base survey data or primary measured survey can be augmented by extra detail or by interpretation.

Measured drawing encompasses two techniques: dimensioned sketches and direct plotting. Dimensioned sketches are the preparation on site of hand-drawn field notes and sketches, annotated with dimensions taken by rod, tape and/or hand-held EDM. These notes can then be constructed directly in CAD or drawn to scale on the drawing board and, if required, digitised into CAD.

This technique allows for rapid gathering of data from a site visit, such that the construction detail, form and function of a building can be determined with a minimum of specialist equipment.

Dimensioned sketches are highly interpretative. The practitioner, using experience and type-specific knowledge, decides which dimensions will be measured and those that will not. The final survey drawing will be based upon the dimensioned sketches and the surveyor's understanding of the structure, often backed up with photographs. If the practitioner is not familiar with the architectural form the survey may not constitute an adequate archive for future examination of the structural history of a building.

Typical survey field notes:

- are of a minimum A3 size, on cartridge paper or plastic film
- include dimension lines shown clearly in red so as to be legible and distinct from clear pencil lines describing the subject
- are sequentially numbered with an indication of the total number of drawings in the set

- should have a title, location diagram, date and author's name marked on each sheet
- represent plumb lines and datum lines in colour or with a broken line
- annotate running or chain lines with control dimensions in a circle and show the overall length of line marked as 'oa'
- indicate tabulation of repetitive or chained measurement with a clear diagram indicating the position, variation of detail, origin, direction and end of line (Fig 20).

There are two major drawbacks of dimensioned sketches: the level of skill required from the practitioner; and the likelihood that a fundamental measurement will be overlooked, necessitating a time-consuming trip back to the field.

Direct plotting refers to the preparation on site of scaled drawings from measurements of the subject (usually by hand drawing on paper or drafting film, but sometimes directly into CAD). The materials used should be of an archive quality and each

Figure 20
A typical dimensioned sketch.

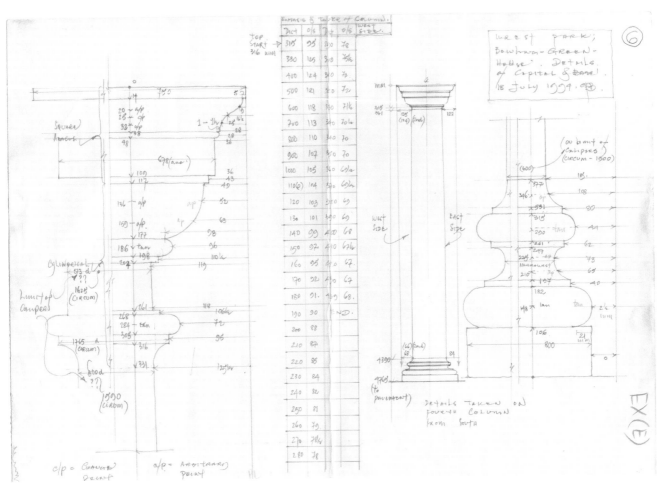

drawing should be labelled with the scale, subject and location diagram. The information for assembling the separate pieces of the drawing (digitising calibration) should be included (eg two coordinated points with their values). Typical drawing scales employed are 1:20 for stone-by-stone drawing of elevations and 1:10 for drawings of complex architectural detail. Recording scale choices vary, however, according to the nature of the subject as well as the intended purpose and output scale (Fig 21).

If a small elevation or part of a building elevation is being recorded in this manner the recording process can be aided by the use of a rigid frame of known internal dimensions held against the wall, one edge being aligned to a baseline. The frame is usually subdivided by strings into 0.20m × 0.20m squares. The frame can be 'flipped' along the baseline to provide a temporary control grid for the wall above and below the baseline. If a 1m × 1m frame is used, baselines across the elevation are needed only at height intervals of 2m (Fig 22).

Direct plotting has one very obvious advantage over dimensioned sketches, in that the drawing is completed before leaving site, reducing the need for repeat visits to obtain missed measurements. This does not mean that all of the desired details will be recorded, however, as the level of detail is a matter for the site-recording brief or practitioner to define. Direct plotting is a labour-intensive technique compared to dimensioned sketching.

Diagnostic diagrams

These are exploded joint and construction details used either to explain aspects of the structure that would not be covered by conventional two-dimensional drawings or to aid the understanding of the building. These diagrams cannot be accurately scaled and do not sit within a site control framework, so other means are required to reference them back to the scaled drawings (Fig 23).

Limitations

There are a number of limitations associated with hand survey:

- missing measurements or detail will require return visits to the site
- lack of type-specific knowledge can result in a flawed survey or an inappropriate record being made

- the survey is highly reliant on the practitioner being skilled at making subjective choices about what to record and what to leave out
- producing the survey requires direct physical access to the subject, as opposed to remote methods such as REDM
- the final drawing is a two-dimensional data set.

Equipment

The equipment required to undertake hand survey is often very personal as individuals develop their own tools and methods in answer to common and new survey dilemmas (eg cutting rulers to a tapered point making it easier to measure mouldings).

Some commonly used tools are:

- measuring tapes, small and large
- plumb bobs
- levels
- balls of string
- small nails
- rulers, including folding rulers
- graphite and coloured pencils
- hand-held brushes
- a rigid frame with a 0.20m grid
- a small trowel.

Control

Like all survey techniques, hand survey requires adequate control if the resulting data is to fit with other data sets, such as pre-existing measured surveys of the building. Control may take a number of forms, ranging from a level line attached to the façade along with a measuring tape to precise three-dimensional survey targets with known co-ordinates measured from a survey control station. The choice of control depends on the degree of precision required and whether or not the hand-survey product is to be integrated with other surveys of the building. Photogrammetry will provide a ready control framework for any direct plotting infill of missing detail or enhancement required.

Control methods often used for hand survey include:

- triangulation (useful for building plans)
- line level, where the survey does not need to fit into a larger data set, or a wire-frame already exists (eg window detail)
- identified points or targets, surveyed in three dimensions to enable hand-recorded data to fit into a larger overall survey (eg where photogrammetric cover is unachievable)

FISHING M
LOOKING
GREYFRIA
KINGS LY1
SCALE 1:

- wire-frame, where the survey can be tied to existing drawings of the outline of a wall
- use of an existing metric survey such as photogrammetry, output at the relevant scale and used as the basis for recording direct-plotting annotation and infill.

Appropriate use

Hand survey becomes cost-effective when applied to

- situations where complex details such as mouldings need to be recorded
- sites where the record needs to be verified as it is created
- structures that are inaccessible to instruments and cameras.

It is also well suited to surveys where the surveyor must capture and interpret construction details that are too small to be visible from the distances found in instrument and camera surveys. It is therefore often employed either as dimensioned sketching for rapid site-recording, or as a secondary

'infill' process to enhance the product of other machine-based surveys through strategic application. Fine detail or mouldings can be represented by other survey methods, but it is only with the intimacy afforded by the close contact of hand survey that measurements can be taken to allow such detail to be recognisably represented.

3.2.4 Laser scanning

A laser scanner can be thought of as a high speed REDM, providing an automated reflectorless capture system that collects mass three-dimensional data. There are two systems in common use: one is based on LiDAR (Light Detection And Ranging) technology and is typically used for medium to long-range projects (>5m), while the other is based on the 'structured light' principle and is typically used for close-range projects (<5m) such as artefact recording.

LiDAR-based scanners emit a series of infra-red measurement beams in an array, using automated sweeps. The intensity, speed and array type depend on the device used. They produce a three-dimensional point 'cloud' of data that requires processing to supply surface and reflectance information from the scanned scene. Point accuracy is typically in the range of 5–25mm. Close-range laser scanners consist of a laser and a charge coupled device (CCD). The CCD is used to record the displacement of a stripe of laser light projected onto the object. The fixed geometry between laser and CCD enables simple triangulation to determine position measurement. Point accuracy is typically in the range of 0.2–2mm.

Laser scanners are effective three-dimensional surface mappers for a variety of

Figure 21
Directly plotted detail. This corbel was originally drawn at a scale of 1:1. The drawing was then digitised and inserted into a sectional elevation using an REDM wire-frame for control, in a process similar to that described for Figure 19.

Figure 22
Recording a wall using a rigid recording frame.

Figure 23
A diagnostic diagram from
a hand survey undertaken
on the crown joint of the
Iron Bridge.

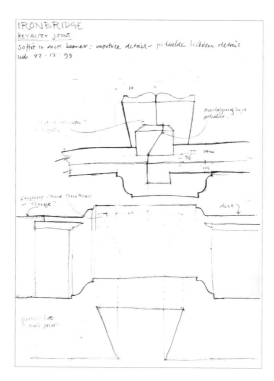

features, including caves, standing stones, statuary, quarry faces and tunnels, because they can supply large volumes of data rapidly and with predictable precision. The use of scanners adapted for the three-dimensional recording of artefacts at close-range and at very high densities is a successful method of recording statuary. The close ranges possible with artefact scanners improve the reliability of the technique. The use of these devices for architectural recording is developing and, although costly, can be effective for surface recording.

The cost of equipment and the need to process huge 'clouds' of three-dimensional data, means that laser scanning is an expensive technique. Laser scanning is also susceptible to distance distortion factors in the same way as REDM: target reflectance, obliqueness and range will affect an unknown number of the points in the scene. As these are automated systems, the operator cannot verify the data sets at the time of capture. Some devices use video imagery of the scene to aid interpretation of the recorded data, but this is no substitute for photogrammetric images.

Laser scanning is best suited to the capture of surface information; the technique is unsuitable for subjects where edge definition is important. For example, architectural subjects such as façades are better dealt with by photogrammetry (*see* Figs 46 and 47). Increasing point densities will not guarantee improved data sets as, in most cases, edge detection is characteristically poor across the range of point densities available.

The handling of three-dimensional data-clouds for the production of CAD models can be a difficult and costly process. It requires software suites specifically developed to handle the high point densities in order to generate usable data. This often requires feature extraction, planar analysis and modelling to be useful to the conservation profession. Drawings that compare with photogrammetric drawings are not readily available from laser scans. The edges and mouldings that characterise architecture are indistinct in the data-cloud and the extraction of such edges from the data-cloud without using additional information from a measured drawing is, at present, almost impossible. Surfaces like boat hulls and curved or battered walls are difficult to describe other than as surfaces. Laser scanning, especially when used in conjunction with photogrammetric survey, is an ideal mapping technique for these types of surfaces.

4

Procurement

The precise three-dimensional recording of historic buildings is a particular application of metric survey that differs from general practice. The required scale for historic-building drawings is greater by a factor of ten than even the most detailed topographic surveys and most metric surveyors are unfamiliar with the drawing conventions used. When commissioning a survey of a historic building it is therefore advisable to describe the required services with care and, once the survey is in hand, to monitor the process carefully.

Procurement issues for metric survey fall into three main areas:

- is the proposed survey method appropriate?
- does the service provider have the right skills?
- does the survey brief include site-specific variables and does it clearly indicate what is expected of the final product: for example, what the survey should look like? (*See* Appendix 1.)

4.1 The survey brief

The client should clearly set out the objectives of the project in the brief to the contractor. Although the responsibility for devising the brief resides with the client, it will benefit from the advice of both survey specialists and historic-building analysts. An effective brief will

- define the purpose of the recording project
- describe how the survey output will be used
- outline the proposed survey techniques, elevation by elevation if necessary
- define the programme of works and the timing of survey activities within the programme, including access, site preparation and scaffolding requirements
- describe the extent, scale and intensity of the survey, and include a clear relevant example of the treatment of detail.

Variation of detail cover proportional to scale should be shown by example if needed
- note the practicalities of power, light, access and personnel contacts.

Once the brief has been prepared it can be issued to one or more specialist survey contractors, who will respond with specifications and costs. Alternatively, the brief can be issued with a technical specification to which the contractor is expected to adhere. A survey specification should leave no doubts as to the outcome of the project. It will determine both the content and quality of the product.

4.2 Survey specification

The survey specification is either designed at the beginning of a programme in response to the brief or issued with the brief at the beginning of the project. The specification will

- describe the acceptable tolerances for the job. This will include the relevant scale tolerances required
- include a safety procedure and professional indemnity
- include a method statement describing the proposed technique and its likely performance
- include a resource statement that should describe not only the equipment and its condition (calibration certification, etc) but also the procedures, skills and personnel to be applied
- specify the system control to be used. This may require Scheduled Monument Consent for station markers. Interested bodies should be encouraged to collaborate in siting permanent ground markers on sensitive sites. The difficulty of using an existing site control is often overlooked; it is worth considering the use of GPS to determine OSNG values
- list the survey products; the specification of the CAD protocols, plot size, line weights, etc needs to be undertaken with

care, particularly where presentation drawings are important or if the data is to be manipulated by others. The archive quality of the output material must be considered. The number of copies and where the final product is to be sent must also be specified.

Metric Survey Specifications for English Heritage (2000) is used by English Heritage to procure metric survey. To date, it has proved a valuable and robust control for the provision of base mapping data in conservation and recording projects for and on behalf of English Heritage. Standard specifications should always be used with care, however, and survey products should never be selected without careful consideration.

Metric Survey Specifications for English Heritage is available at a cost of £15 from the following address:

English Heritage Postal Sales
Gillards
Trident Works
Temple Cloud
Bristol BS39 5AZ
Tel: 01761 452966
(Product code 50562)

5
Case studies

5.1 Battle Abbey courthouse: an archaeological survey

The Central Archaeology Service (CAS) of English Heritage – now the Centre for Archaeology (CfA) – became involved in a series of projects at Battle Abbey starting with excavations in 1990. These investigations centred on the gatehouse structure (Fig 24), which is made up of three buildings: the 14th-century gatehouse in the centre, the 16th-century courthouse on the left as viewed from the town and the earlier Norman gatehouse on the right (Hare 1985, 13 and CfA archives). When it was decided to convert the courthouse into the main visitor entrance to the site, the CAS was asked to record the historic fabric and conduct excavations in order to aid the design of the new works and help in the interpretation of the historic building.

5.1.1 Site survey

The proposals for the shell entailed consolidation and repair of the standing fabric, as well as building a new roof- and floor-bearing structure inside that was to be independent of the historic walls. A detailed drawn record was needed both to serve the architects and to allow archaeological interpretation of the building. To this end, in 1992 a photogrammetric survey was undertaken by the English Heritage Photogrammetric Unit as the most economical way to produce a basic record of the standing walls.

As Figure 25 shows, the primary measured survey in this case took place under less than ideal conditions, since there were patches of vegetation on the masonry and areas of bricked-up detail in the windows. Because the primary measured survey was required before any remedial work to clear these obstructions could be carried out, it was left to the hand-survey component of the project to record the missing detail.

The elevation drawings were enhanced by hand-survey techniques to provide an accurate stone-by-stone record of each wall. This elevation record was augmented as

Figure 24
Battle Abbey courthouse, viewed from the High Street.

27

Figure 25
The interior of the
courthouse showing
vegetation at wall-head
level and the shell of the
squash court.

Figure 26
Scaffolding of the Battle
Abbey gatehouse, from
which detailed
archaeological investigation
and recording of the
structure were carried out.

excavations in and adjacent to the shell revealed the footings of the walls and other now-vanished structures. As the photogrammetric plotting was captured digitally in three dimensions and supplied in AutoCAD R12 format, manageable portions of the elevations could be plotted on to paper for use out on site. The entire structure was scaffolded to allow access (Fig 26) and a team of six archaeologists spent six weeks comparing each plotted elevation to the fabric of the building and drawing overlays of corrections and additional information that would aid interpretation.

5.1.2 CAD

The CAD elevations had a 1m grid superimposed on them to aid alignment of the individual correction sheets. Each elevation was then plotted out at a scale of 1:20 as a series of 5m × 5m tiles on A3 sheets of archive-quality paper. These were taped to plywood boards, overlain with drafting film and taken up on to the scaffolding for direct comparison to the fabric of the walls. Any differences between the plots and the real fabric were marked, as were material types, weathering and other features such as grooves, cracks and nails (Fig 27).

To take advantage of the three-dimensional nature of the primary photogrammetric data as delivered in CAD, the corrections were digitised into the CAD drawings at appropriate three-dimensional coordinates to match the surrounding masonry. Within each drawing as supplied there was a coordinate system that used horizontal distance across the drawing as the x-axis, distance up the drawing as the y-axis and distance out from an arbitrary plane behind the drawing as the z-axis. As these axes were used when laying on the 1m grid for the paper plots, these 'elevation' coordinate systems in effect provided the survey control for the hand survey. The z-axis defined the surface texture of the wall and represented the one axis not recorded by the hand-drawn corrections.

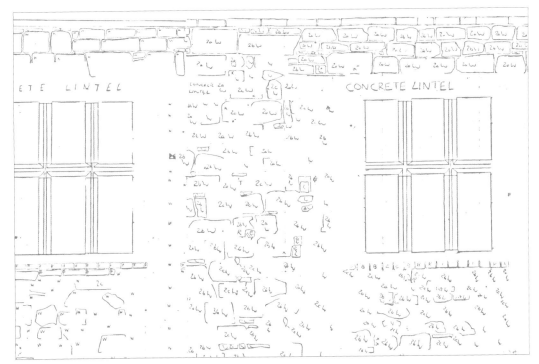

Figure 27 (left)
Detail of a hand-drawn
overlay of corrections on a
plot of photogrammetry.
Note the extent of the
revision on the stones
between the windows. The
3-character codes on the
stones record weathering
and damage against a
pre-set glossary.

Figure 28 (below)
An isometric view of
photogrammetric data with
digitised corrections
recorded in two dimensions.
In this example,
photogrammetric UCS puts
the wall face at an
elevation of 10.

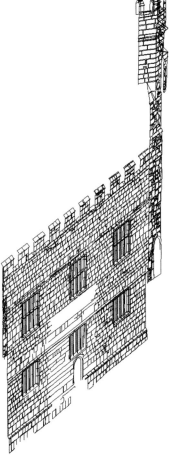

Figure 28 is an isometric view of data digitised in the traditional two-dimensional manner, while Figure 29 shows corrected three-dimensional data assembled to form a model of the building for analytical and presentational purposes. The x- and y-axes were generated from the digitising tablet, but the z-axis needed to be derived from the existing CAD files. To achieve the desired effect, detail points near the corrections were interrogated to find the missing axis values to the nearest millimetre and the new points were digitised at the appropriate z-value to match. This provided both accurate corrected two-dimensional elevation plots and relatively accurate corrected three-dimensional modelling of the structure at a later date.

In Figure 30 one of the internal elevations is shown with the uncorrected data on the left, the finished product on the right and the hand-measured corrections in the centre as bold lines with the raw data shaded below. Note how the wall-head, which had been capped as a ledge within the ruin, was completely obscured at the time of the photogrammetric survey and had to be recorded entirely by hand. Note also how a number of stones that were either in shadow or otherwise indistinct in the photographs had to be redrawn. Typical problems included cracked stones being drawn as two separate stones by the photogrammetrist and the omission of small details such as tiles used as packing. In many instances, the details could only be

Figure 29
An isometric view of the interior of the Battle Abbey courthouse, as used on site information boards during excavations in 1993 and 1994.

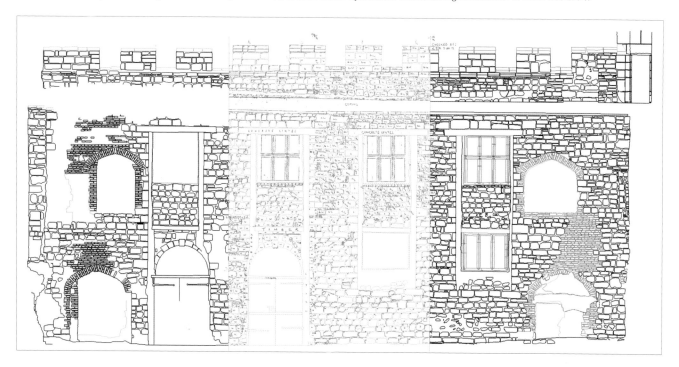

Figure 30
A composite elevation showing raw photogrammetry, hand-drawn corrections and the completed model.

seen upon close inspection. Figure 27 shows the overlaid hand corrections and the primary photogrammetry data. While the building's exterior ashlar faces required fairly minor revisions, approximately 25 per cent of the fabric of the coursed-rubble interior faces needed some form of correction, alteration or enhancement.

In conclusion, the Battle Abbey courthouse project required a combination of photogrammetric and hand-survey techniques to create a product that not only satisfied the needs of the architects but also those of the building analysts and the Inspector of Ancient Monuments.

5.2 Danson House: a scale hand survey

Danson House in Bexley, London, was built between 1763 and 1766 to the designs of Sir Robert Taylor. It is a prime example of a villa designed by a leading exponent of the Palladian movement in England. Much of the original detail survives and the house is currently undergoing restoration by English Heritage.

5.2.1 Hand survey

The library cornice was drawn by hand at a scale of 1:2, on site, on an A4 sheet of grid paper, by a practitioner working from a scaffolding tower (Figs 31 and 32). As a section drawing, however, it is a composite: at no point in the room was the cornice wholly sawn through and exposed in one single section. The drawing is therefore an assemblage of a set of observations made at various points around the room.

Besides the profiles of the plaster mouldings, the drawing records constructional details such as the lath and timber formers on which the cornice was run. Applied to the laths was a base coat of white lime plaster (which included lumps of lime up to 8mm in size and some animal hair) approximately 22mm thick. A skim of white lime plaster was applied to the base coat. The finished plaster wall face was about 85mm proud of the brick wall face. This detailed construction information is significant in determining whether or not the cornice dates from the first fitting-out scheme within the room and thus is the work of Robert Taylor.

The profile and proportions are important for the architectural historical analysis of the cornice. Comparison with drawings of similar cornices enables the identification of historical precedents and influences. The plaster cornice is of the Doric order and ultimately derived from the Theatre of Marcellus in Rome. This cornice appears, however, to have stimulated some debate among those who illustrated it and Taylor's version at Danson is no doubt a personal interpretation. Serlio illustrated it in *The Five Books of Architecture* (Book 4, fol 18), with the cavetto at the top but the mutules recessed and horizontal. The lower parts were also recorded very differently. It seems Taylor took Palladio's model Doric cornice, based on the Theatre of Marcellus example and illustrated as Plate xv in Book I of *The Four Books of Architecture* (Fig 33). He adhered to Palladio's model in all respects except for the projection of the mutule course and in the use of a cavetto in place of the greater cimatium. Isaac Ware reproduced his version in Plate xvii in *A Complete Body of Architecture* and, it seems, like Palladio, considered the use of the cavetto at the top of the cornice an error based on a misinterpretation of Vitruvius's text.

Figure 31
The plaster cornice and frieze in the library at Danson House.

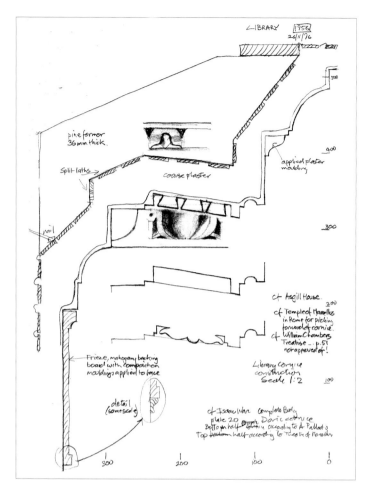

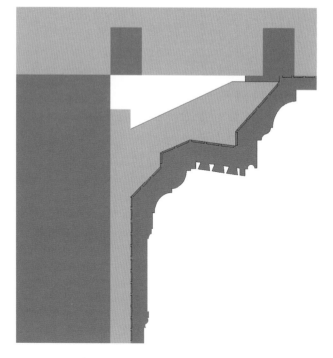

0   500mm

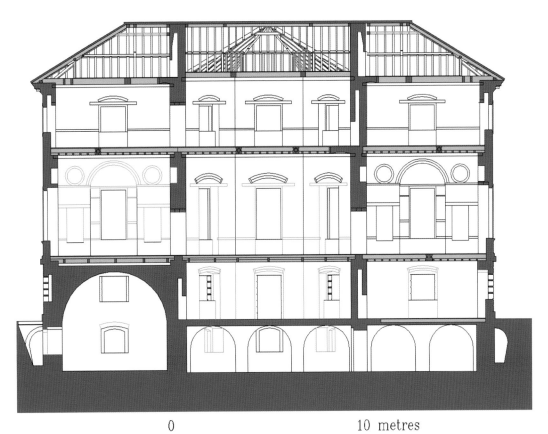

Figure 32
(facing page, top left)
Hand drawing of the
cornice and frieze.

Figure 33
(facing page, top right)
Palladio's drawing of a
Doric cornice from
The Four Books of
Architecture.

Figure 34
(facing page, bottom)
The drawing of the cornice
translated into an
AutoCAD detail drawing.

Figure 35 (left)
An AutoCAD section
through Danson House
showing the building as
completed in c 1765 before
fitting-out. Here, the
cornice drawing is included
as a detail.

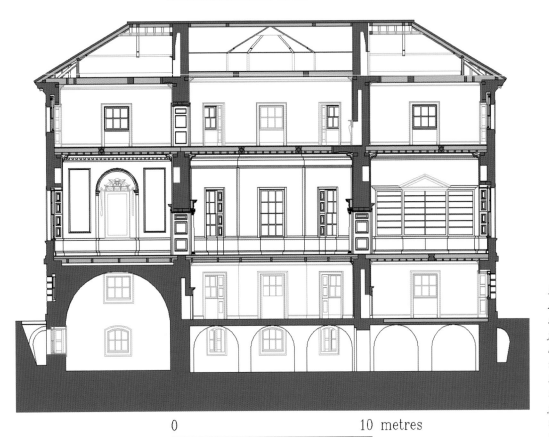

0   10 metres

Figure 36
An AutoCAD section
showing the house after
fitting-out in c 1766. The
library is the first-floor
room with the bookcases.
Note how the fitting-out of
the principal floor does not
fit exactly with the
masonry shell as shown in
Figure 35.

33

Figure 37
One of the twenty-five
boards that make up the
Dauntsey Doom Board,
showing a significant loss of
fabric.

William Chambers, however, accepted the use of the cavetto but objected to the mutules hanging down. He reproduced the cornice with the ornament in the horizontal position. This analysis demonstrates not only the importance of Palladio for the architect Robert Taylor and his generation, but also the ways in which Taylor felt it appropriate to interpret the Classical precedents.

The timber and composition frieze below the cornice is a 19th-century addition incorporating a repeated arabesque motif. On site, only essential dimensions were taken for this element. The detail was added later in AutoCAD using simple rectified photography and the hand drawing as a control. The outline of the arabesque was then traced from photographs taken flat on (Fig 34).

This drawing forms only part of a detailed survey of the whole house. Once transferred to AutoCAD it was simplified and used in several larger section drawings through the whole house (Figs 35 and 36).

5.3 Dauntsey Doom Board: the use of rectified photography

In October 1998 the photogrammetric unit of English Heritage was approached by the historic buildings architect for the South-West Region of English Heritage to provide a photographic record of the Doom Board from the Church of St James the Great at Dauntsey, near Chippenham in Wiltshire.

Rectified photography was selected as the survey technique, as it provided a cost-effective image-based method of recording the Doom Board prior to its eventual return and rehanging within Dauntsey church. This survey method is ideally suited to non-three-dimensional surfaces such as painted oak boards.

The Doom Board now comprises twenty-five painted oak boards (Figs 37 and 38). At the start of the survey, rather than forming one complete unit, the twenty-five boards had already been separated, as they had been removed from the church to undergo conservation treatment. Some of the original boards were missing and others had suffered physical loss, principally from the edges, which meant that there was some uncertainty regarding the Doom Board's final arrangement. It was hoped that rectified photography could help determine the

original layout. Rather than providing individual images for a manual 'cut and pasting' exercise, it was decided to use digital rectified photography to assemble a 'virtual' montage that could be manipulated on a computer screen.

5.3.1 Recording issues

The twenty-five individual oak boards had been restored at a conservator's workshop in Corpusty near Norwich. They had been laid out on the studio floor in what was thought to be their correct positions. Limited working

Figure 38
The Doom Board laid out
at the conservation studio.

To give the darkroom printer or the digital-scanning operator a reference from which to work, an industry-standard Kodak colour chart was placed in each photograph taken.

A medium-format 120-roll film camera with a 90mm lens was used for the photography. Given the circumstances this was considered the most appropriate format for the project because of its greater flexibility over the larger 5in. × 4in. format. In addition, the final enlargement factor, from negative up to final 1:10 print scale, was also well within the capability of the arrangement making it possible to have imagery without any loss of definition.

Kodak NC 120 professional film was chosen: NC for its ability to represent neutral colour and to not give bias to any dye; and professional film for its good batch colour consistency.

space meant that the original idea of photographing the whole arrangement of boards from above had to be discarded. Placing a camera vertically over a large body of work was not practical or safe for the photographer or the boards, because of the risks of tripods or other surrounding objects slipping.

Another difficulty was that of illuminating the boards evenly. The original idea of using the existing natural light already coming through the workshop's skylights had to be rejected as the light would be uneven and exposure would have to wait until there was sufficient cloud cover outside to minimise shadows and flare. In addition, the surface of the boards had been treated with what appeared to be a highly reflective varnish, which created a vast number of highlights when the boards were viewed from differing positions. It was essential, therefore, that the chosen illumination technique could be fully controlled.

5.3.3 Control method

To provide an accurate scale to the final rectified images, the individual boards needed some form of control data. Placing targets on the surface of the painted oak was not possible because this might damage the boards. It would also have been very time consuming for a surveyor to observe detail points on each of the twenty-five boards.

Instead, a large plain background panel was used as a frame and, by attaching to it small blocks of wood that were the thickness of the Doom Board itself, one common set of control was provided to each of the panels as they were consecutively placed within the frame. Black and white self-adhesive targets of 1cm diameter were placed on each of the six small wooden blocks. The distances between each of these targets were then measured in two braced quadrilateral arrangements, using a steel tape. Then, using simple trigonometry, two-dimensional coordinates were computed, based on a reference value of 10 for the lower left-hand target; this ensured that all the values would be positive (Figs 39 and 40).

5.3.2 Photography method

Bearing the above problems in mind, it was decided to create a small photographic copy set-up in the conservator's workshop and photograph each board separately. Two electronic flash units were used and fitted with soft boxes. This provided the ability to control what light was falling on the subject and at what angle, reducing the chances of highlights reflecting off the shiny varnish finish. Using a professional flash system also provided a colour consistency of 5500K (Kelvin), the colour temperature of daylight. This matched the colour temperature of the film and would provide accurate results.

5.3.4 Rectification and digital manipulation

All exposed film was processed through a quality-controlled professional laboratory to ensure consistency in the colour reproduction of the dyes in the base emulsion. To provide digital copy, each negative was scanned on to Pro PhotoCD™ (Eastman Kodak Company). This enabled the digital-image

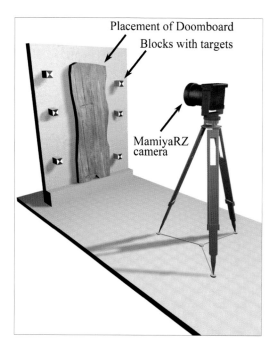

Placement of Doomboard

Blocks with targets

MamiyaRZ camera

rectified they were imported into Adobe PhotoShop® for cropping and balancing. Prior to final montaging in Adobe Photo-Shop® each one of the rectified images was imported into AutoCAD R14 for viewing and manipulation. This facility was used with advice from the historic buildings architect and the project architect to help determine the most appropriate board arrangement, based upon the visible evidence.

Adobe PhotoShop® was used because it provides the user with the facility to edit the background and leave it transparent, thus enabling several different layers of information to be manipulated. Each one of the twenty-five doom boards was assigned its own layer, which made it simple to rearrange the board and position it accurately to form the final montage as shown in Figure 42.

5.3.5 Conclusions

This work was completed to a very high standard and the end-product, importantly, was what the conservation team required. The control used, although provided by simple steel tapes, was economic, robust and precise enough for the rectification process and had no impact on the fragile boards. Since this work, improvements have been made on colour control by adding a Macbeth colour chart into photographs (an industry standard). It is apparent that people

files to be loaded into an image-manipulation programme, such as Adobe PhotoShop® (Adobe Systems Incorporated). The rectification of each image was carried out using the MSR software package from Rolleimetric (Fig 41).

Using the computed two-dimensional coordinates, each image was digitally rectified on screen and a scale was attached to each of the digital files. When all of the twenty-five images had been individually

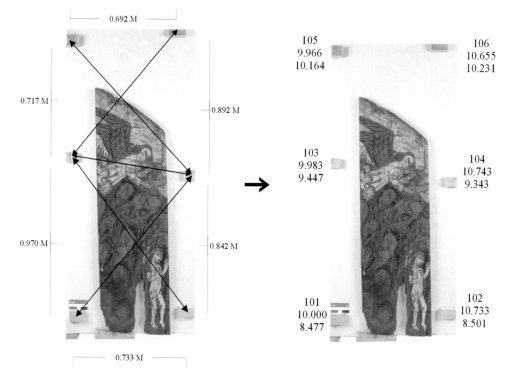

0.692 M

0.717 M   0.892 M

0.970 M   0.842 M

0.733 M

105
9.966
10.164

106
10.655
10.231

103
9.983
9.447

104
10.743
9.343

101
10.000
8.477

102
10.733
8.501

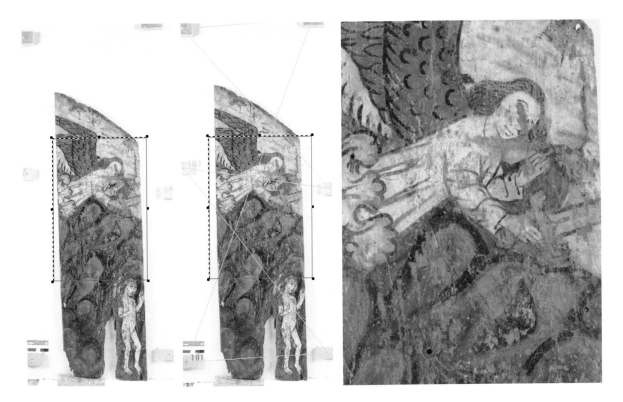

Figure 41
The digital rectification process using MSR software from Rolleimetric.

Figure 42
The final montaged rectified image.

with limited knowledge of the overall photographic process have little idea of what makes an accurate record – for example, there is an assumption that available natural light is adequate to illuminate the work. As in most location work the photographer has to adapt to the surroundings, especially when the image is required for the conservation process and to provide a record for the national archive.

5.4 Measuring the Iron Bridge

The Iron Bridge at Coalbrookdale (Fig 43) was scheduled as an Ancient Monument in 1934 and is the centrepiece of the World Heritage Site designated by a United Nations Education, Scientific and Cultural Organisation (UNESCO) charter in 1986. The bridge is the world's earliest major iron span and was the prototype for iron-bridge construction. It is of great importance as the first structure to use iron on an industrial scale and

the manufacture of its components is a unique example of the quality-controlled production of iron as a building material in the 18th century.

The bridge is constructed of large cast-iron parts (the largest weighing up to 5.5 tonnes) cast, positioned and fitted in 1779 under the direction of Abraham Darby III, master iron-founder, and Thomas Gregory, his pattern-maker. The form of the bridge is derived from a design by Thomas Farnolls Pritchard, the architect directed by the bridge commissioners in 1776. There is no surviving copy of Pritchard's drawing other than early scheme drawings for iron spans, so it is an open question as to how much of the erected structure is from Pritchard's design and how much is a result of foundry pattern work. The historic central span of cast iron is 30.12m long. It is made up of five frames supporting a roadway of forty-two cast deck-plates. The span is an arch of a near-perfect semicircle standing on stone abutments. The deck rises at an angle of

Figure 43
The Iron Bridge at Coalbrookdale. This was the world's first major iron-span bridge, erected in 1779 under the direction of Abraham Darby.

approximately 5 degrees to a shallow arc joining the two pitched sides of the deck.

In 1999, as surface corrosion had become extensive, the bridge was in need of painting. It was also found that there had been some loss of the bearing between the deck-bearers and the deck, which required consolidation.

5.4.1 Metric survey requirement

The proposed works needed metric survey drawings for scaffolding design, marking-up the painting regime and recording repairs. Metric survey was also used for the following purposes:

- to verify the historic 1977 photogrammetric survey. Although this survey was incomplete because there were obscured areas in the photographs, the opportunity was taken to use the work in the new survey
- to enter data from archaeological investigation on to 1:50 ink-on-plastic photogrammetric plots in order to provide a precise base for recording the type and phase of the bridge components in two dimensions
- to acquire a better understanding of the structure. There are many gaps in our knowledge of both the design and construction phases of the bridge; the three-dimensional record enabled theories to be tested against true-to-scale information
- to provide visitors with virtual and on-site interpretation of the bridge through the use of three-dimensional survey data and high-resolution CAD models, thus enabling them to observe the structure from different viewpoints. This would not be possible in any other medium
- to record the repair histories of the bridge components in a three-dimensional framework so as to enable the survey data to be used as a GIS for informing future projects
- to map the twists caused by post-erection deformation, thus providing a stress analysis for the bridge and enabling locations of future failure to be identified.

The structure had undergone a number of movements since its erection in 1779. The rotational thrust between the abutments and the pressure of the unconstrained stonework led to a rebuild of the approach arches in 1821 and, in 1972–3, below-water ferro-concrete

retaining work had to be carried out because of the continued movement of the footings. As a result, the shape of the frames spanning the river had been distorted. Survey was needed to record the frames in their present state so as to enable them to be monitored over time and for any future movement to be understood.

A number of the original castings had cracked or snapped as a result of the above stresses. The failure and subsequent repair or replacement of components revealed that much of the movement take-up had occurred prior to 1973. The snapping of the radials on the south side of the span, the compression of the chords of the main ribs and the displacement and twist across the deck were all recorded to a consistent three-dimensional positional precision of ±25mm for the model and ±10mm in the photogrammetric wire-frame.

5.4.2 Survey techniques

Control

A prerequisite of producing a complete survey of the bridge was the use of a common control. Thirteen stations were set out on an adjusted traverse. These were then used to ensure that the data produced by the different survey techniques was compatible. Control for photogrammetry required the stations to be occupied for the recording of 600 control points on the bridge. Observation was carried out by two-point intersection to detail points on the structure rather than marked targets.

Metric survey methods

The Iron Bridge presents a number of problems to the surveyor: the need for a wide range of scales from large (1:50) to small (full size); line-of-sight obstructions and access affected all the applied techniques; and lighting and vegetation were difficulties for photo-based techniques. When access was possible by scaffolding, instrument and hand-survey techniques could be used. Nevertheless, gaps in the data set remained. Filling these gaps provided the team with an opportunity to evaluate the performance of laser scanning when applied to the rigorous levels of precision required for the survey of a historic structure of this kind.

Photogrammetry

Stereo-photography for photogrammetry was acquired from camera positions on the

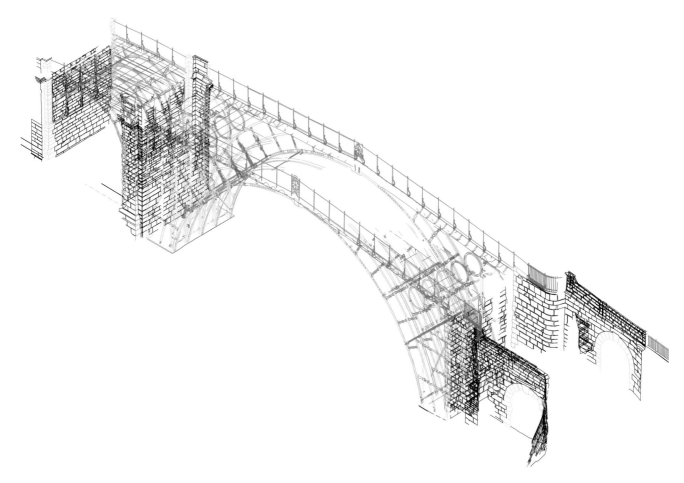

Figure 44

The wire-frame plotted from photogrammetry. The lack of cover is the result of vegetation, near-camera obstructions, limited access and poor lighting obscuring the lines of sight.

[Photogrammetric survey by PCA Ltd]

riverbank and also under the bridge at the footings, lit by available daylight. Vegetation obstructing sight lines from the riverbank and obscuring the retaining façades required the supplementary use of historic (1972) stereo-photography. Limited access, poor lighting and near-camera obstructions obscured the soffit of the span and meant that there was no cover of the soffit at the centre of the span (Fig 44). The camera used in both cases was a Wild P31 at a range of approximately 40m and a Zeiss UMK 300mm for ranges exceeding 40m.

The wire-frame is three dimensional but rarely plots all the possible edges of the components because of line-of-sight obstructions, poorly lit imagery or indistinct edges. The consistency of precision in the wire-frame is an inherent property of photogrammetry. Note the soffit of the deck (*see* Fig 44): there is little or no information here because of the deep shadow in which the soffit lay at the time of photography.

REDM

When access by scaffolding was possible, REDM was used to fill in the gaps in the

photogrammetric wire-frame. Stations were set up on the scaffolding between each frame and ties to the photogrammetric wire-frame were made by resection to detail. By using instrument set-ups under the deck gaps could be infilled at close range. All the REDM data was recorded in real-time into AutoCAD using TheoLT on a field computer, a process that can be described as three-dimensional digitising (Fig 45).

Isometric sketches and narrative photography

Isometric sketches were needed to record and understand the fitting of the jointing and the engineering detail of hidden parts that were not visible in the elevational drawing (*see* Fig 23). Narrative close-up photography was also taken of all of the joints and indexed by component.

Laser scanning

Laser scans were taken to infill the deck soffit not mapped by REDM or photogrammetry. The data-cloud was modelled and prepared for insertion into CAD through the use of automated surface extraction software.

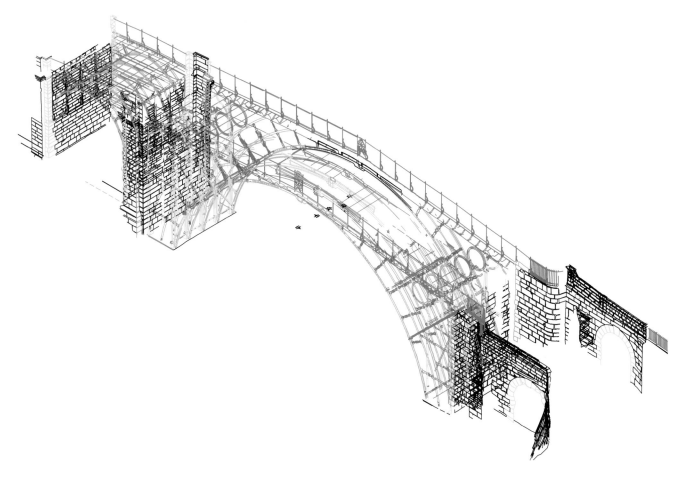

The laser scan was unable to supply any edge definition of components that could be generated to the required tolerance. The main value of the data was to add to patches of information on the surfaces between the wire-frame edges and to determine the surface profiles of the lower parts of the main ribs. The data received from the laser scan was generally less useful than that produced by photogrammetry.

The data-cloud from the laser scan (Figs 46 and 47) could only be used for surface interpolation. The mapping of edges was not possible because of the low density of the data-cloud and the skewing of distance values caused by multiple signal reflection.

Measured two-dimensional drawing

Two-dimensional details of the bridge's joints were recorded on site by plotting the measured detail directly on to 1:50 scale elevation plots. To maintain vertical control for this, string-levelled lines were used to transfer data from plot to plot. The pencil annotations were then inked in. Ironbridge Gorge Museum Trust Archaeology, under the direction of Shelly White, plotted evidence for the

sequence of casting and assembly on to ink-on-plastic plots supplied from photogrammetry. The plotted evidence was subsequently used for the archaeological analysis.

5.4.3 Constructing the solid model from the wire-frame CAD model

Because the wire-frame from photogrammetry and REDM survey was built on a common control and CAD platform it could be used to form and fit solid components in true three-dimensional positions. It was decided to use solid rather than surface modelling for the following reasons:

- edge extraction – a solid model will allow the extraction of line drawings without disruption by surface meshes
- file size is reduced compared to the surface model equivalent
- component fitting and counterpart modelling is possible using Boolean operations; the fit between parts can be used to create the edges of components
- element analysis is possible.

Figure 45
The wire-frame completed by REDM. The precision of the REDM work was adequate to model the deformation of the arcs for all five main ribs. The deck-plate edges were digitised in three dimensions and the distortion of the deck recorded. (Compare this to the photogrammetric wire-frame in Figure 44.)

Figure 46
The data-cloud from the
laser scan of the Iron
Bridge.
[Laser scan by UK Robotic
Ltd]

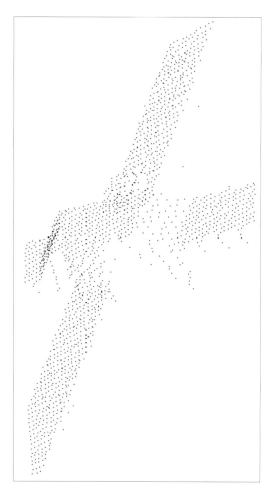

Figure 46
The data-cloud from the
laser scan of the Iron
Bridge.
[Laser scan by UK Robotic
Ltd]

By building up closed regions from the wire-frame, solid parts were extruded into their true coordinate positions in space. Components were replicated and tested to fit the housings for the new position. Most of the joints have generous passing tolerances so it was surprising to find that many parts could not be fitted in this way. Most of the radial links between the ribs are one-offs suggesting that many castings were made to retro fit locations, ie to fit the spaces left in the structure during construction. The distortion of the main ribs is such that a reflection from one quadrant to its opposite is not possible. The simple arc sections used for the ribs are subject to tilt and twist and careful interpolation of the wire-frame was needed here to develop solid components (Figs 48 and 49).

Modelling conventions and parameters

Modelling the bridge required a compromise between model integrity and CAD performance. The bridge comprises some 1,420 cast parts (excluding fixings and fasteners): to model all the parts and their variants as full-size replicas would have generated a file size of approximately 500 megabytes, unusable without extensive computer resources. It was decided that there should be a tolerance of up to 35mm surface-to-edge variation to economise on

Figure 47
Automatic surface
generation from the laser-
scan data-cloud. The
mouldings of the castings
have been corrupted
beyond recognition. The
generated surfaces are seen
here exported into
AutoCAD.
[Laser scan by UK Robotic
Ltd]

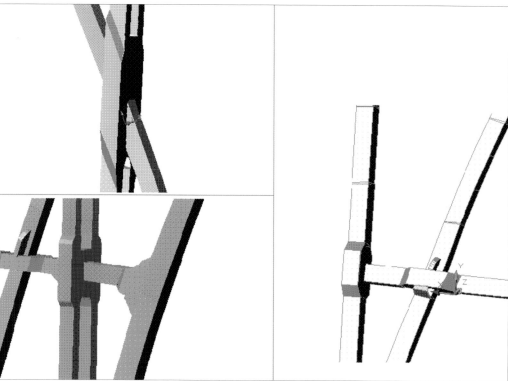

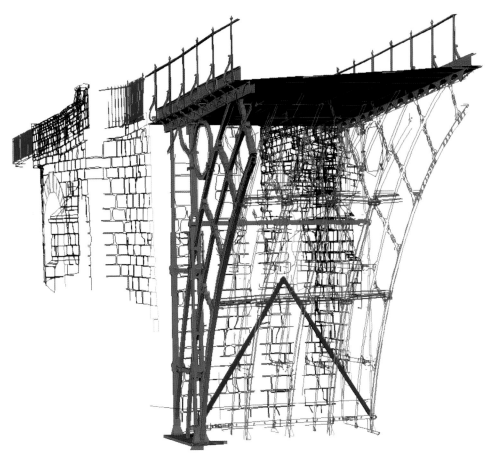

Figure 48
The solid model under
construction. The railing
supports have been copied
into position bounded by
the wire-frame.

surface generation for the solids used. Where it can be inferred that parts have a path through each other, such a path has been interpolated in the model. Many joints are indistinct as they have been caulked with molten lead to fill voids and the internal spaces of the joint housings can only be estimated. As with simpler CAD models and drawings, layering was used to separate the data by location, part name and phase.

5.4.4 Insights and discoveries through metric survey data

Evidence of industrial techniques

The detailed investigation required by the survey showed that various industrial processes had been used to construct the bridge. Evidence was found for the following:

- the use of two casting processes in the manufacture of the bridge components, ie 'Swept-up casting' and 'Closed casting'
- the reuse of counterpart patterns for mortises and passing moulds

- the use of retro-fitted parts
- the development of fixing technologies (Fig 50)
- the orientation and sequence of casting
- variation of pattern quality.

Erection sequence

The constructed CAD model can be used to test erection theories. For example, by fitting views of the model to the 1779 sketch by

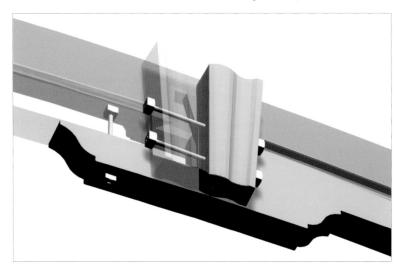

Figure 49
Detail of the crown joint
(see Fig 23) modelled from
site sketches and the
REDM wire-frame. The
joint's overall position and
orientation were determined
from the photogrammetric
wire-frame.

Figure 50
Fixings used to locate and
arrest lateral movement by
the use of shrunk straps.

Elias Martin it is possible to attempt to re-create the sequence of assembly.

Assessment of pre-photographic images/ drawing regression study

Comparison between a matched perspective view in an engraving by William Ellis after M A Rooker (*c* 1782) and the CAD model (Figs 51 and 52) reveals the omission of the central frame details. This omission adds to the evidence that the engraved view was prepared from design drawings rather than from the structure itself.

5.4.5 Effectiveness of survey methods used

Photogrammetry is the most reliable method for mass three-dimensional data capture but it can be compromised by the image quality of the stereo-pair. The production of the wire-frame used in the survey required the provision of a detailed brief for the contractor, who was chosen on the basis of having carried out previous work of this kind. The selection of edges to produce a good three-dimensional wire-frame for complex

historic structures needs to be based on experience underpinned by a sound architectural knowledge.

The infill by REDM matched the wire-frame integrity from photogrammetry. Real-time CAD data collection allowed data selection and checking to a high order of precision and observational accuracy. The selection of edges was informed by real-time checking of the wire-frame on site.

Laser scanning did not supply good edge-fitted modelling for the precision survey of the structure. The captured data from laser scanning takes the form of a data-cloud: the selection of edges to form three-dimensional positions from the cloud tends to corrupt the delineation of the subject. This was exacerbated by automated feature extraction, which resulted in poorer data than that from photogrammetry at the large (1:20–1:10) scales needed to replicate the engineered fit of the bridge components.

The three-dimensional CAD model

The construction of a three-dimensional model allows greater use of the survey data. The mechanical constraints of the bridge can

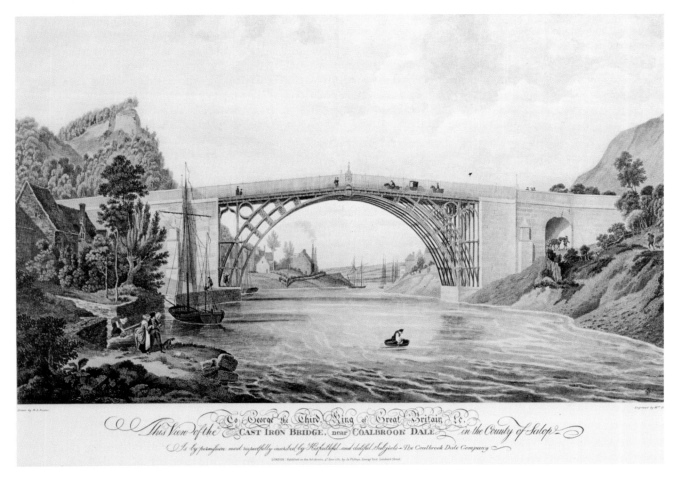

Figure 51
The Cast Iron Bridge near Coalbrookdale, an engraving by William Ellis after M A Rooker, dated 1782. The 'missing ribs' are shown even though they were not in place until 1791 and the central frame casting error is absent; this then is a view worked up in the studio, probably from design drawings.
[© Ironbridge Gorge Museum Trust; 1978.78]

Figure 52
View of the CAD model matched to the view shown in Figure 51 and revealing the casting error on the central frame.

be investigated, and component integrity and failure patterns tested. The three-dimensional model also gives greater scope for the presentation of a well-visited site such as the Iron Bridge: it can be used for virtual reconstruction, construction animations, showing indications of historic *ad hoc* design and explaining the conservation and analytical work that has been undertaken.

5.4.6 Interdisciplinary approaches

Type-specific knowledge is essential for specialist recording: the recording of variations in components, their displacement and other factors should be informed by a knowledge of the design constraints, methods used and known repair regimes. In this case, in-depth knowledge of the history of the bridge focused the survey work on specific details and areas and made it possible to produce animated construction sequences from the three-dimensional model.

5.5 Peterborough Cathedral nave ceiling

The great medieval nave ceiling at Peterborough Cathedral dates from between 1210 and 1230 and is the only 13th-century painted wooden ceiling to survive *in situ* in the United Kingdom (Fig 53). The ceiling is 62m long, 11m wide and canted on each side. It is constructed from overlapping oak boards, held in place by nails driven into joists from below. Attempts over the years to reinforce these fixings have increased the rigidity of the ceiling structure, preventing the natural movement of the wood. This, combined with recent environmental conditions in the cathedral, has caused new structural problems, such as the loosening of some of the original nails and the splitting of boards. The conservation project was aimed at securing the long-term survival and security of the ancient painted boards in their present condition.

In 1994 English Heritage was approached to provide advice to the architect to the Dean and Chapter of Peterborough on the survey requirements for the proposed conservation project. Consultation focused on the potential use of photogrammetric techniques to provide the base survey data for both the architects and the conservators to plan and carry out the required treatments. Discussions initially centred on the production of a suitable specification for a photogrammetric outline survey of the entire ceiling for the Dean and Chapter, which they could then use to procure the required data themselves through a contractor. It soon became apparent, however, that the amount of detail was such that a scaled photographic montage of the whole ceiling would also be required. It was recognised that this project would provide an ideal opportunity to test the application of digital photogrammetric techniques, in particular orthophotography, in a conservation environment. As a result the English Heritage Metric Survey Team became directly involved in the work.

5.5.1 Survey control

At the time of the survey, December 1996, no fixed survey grid existed around the cathedral. Twenty temporary survey stations were therefore set out on a local grid on the triforium, from which observations to control stereo-pairs could be made. Using an EDM, the traverse from the triforium was brought up into the roof space, providing a common three-dimensional control system. Main stations were laid out along the central walkway of the roof and satellite stations were placed to allow a field of sight down the sloping panels to the inaccessible wall-head. It was essential to use the same control system for the roof survey as that used for the ceiling.

Figure 53 (right)
View of Peterborough Cathedral nave.
[© Julian Limentani]

Figure 54
(facing page, top)
A diagram showing the camera and theodolite set-up positions that were used to take and control the stereo-pairs.

To enable each of the twenty-two stereo-models to be orientated in an analytical stereo-plotter or a digital photogrammetric workstation, a minimum of four control points per model was required. Because of the difficulty of placing plastic targets on the ceiling it was decided to use points of detail, even though these would not provide the same clarity of pointing and hence level of accuracy as a target and would also take longer to observe. The wide platform at triforium level was used for surveying the control points by intersection, as it provided both an excellent view of the ceiling and reduced the need for any extreme vertical angle observations (Fig 54). To allow the intersections to be carried out effectively colour prints were made from the stereo-photography and marked up directly on site, as detail points were selected. A total of eighty-five points of detail were coordinated. This meant that there were up to six points available per model. Normally only four points per model are required so these extra control points helped ameliorate the reduced accuracy that was a consequence of using solely detail points.

5.5.2 Stereo-photography

The cathedral ceiling is 25m above ground-floor level. In order to acquire stereo-photography of a suitable negative scale it was necessary for the English Heritage Metric Survey Team to use either access equipment or a camera with a telephoto lens. The use of access equipment was rejected for two reasons. First, there was the physical difficulty of bringing a scaffolding tower or hydraulic lift into the cathedral. Secondly, the photography had to make use of available light, since artificial methods would not have given adequate illumination over the whole ceiling. The long exposure times thus involved made the use of access equipment impossible, as it would not have been sufficiently stable. The decision was therefore taken to use a Zeiss UMK 30/1318 metric camera for the photography.

The 5in. × 7in. format and 300mm lens of the UMK meant that the entire width of the ceiling could be covered in one photograph taken from the ground floor (*see* Fig 54). The resulting negative scale of approximately 1:80 was sufficient to allow the production of drawings at 1:20 or even 1:10. The camera and tripod were mounted on a 'dolly' and wheeled down the centre of the nave, making possible a run of twenty-three

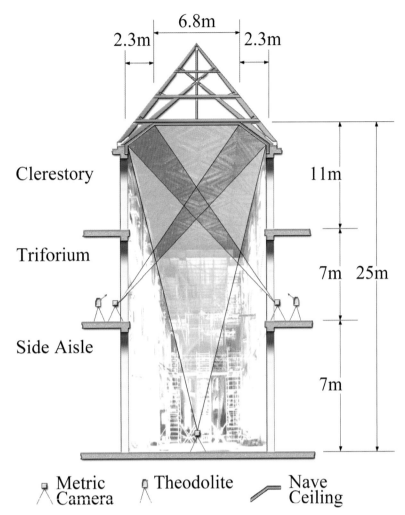

photographs and thus twenty-two stereo-models (Fig 55). In addition to this ground-based photography, stereo-imagery was taken from the triforium using a 5in. × 4in. format WILD P31 metric camera with a

Figure 55 (below)
A stereo-pair of the nave ceiling.

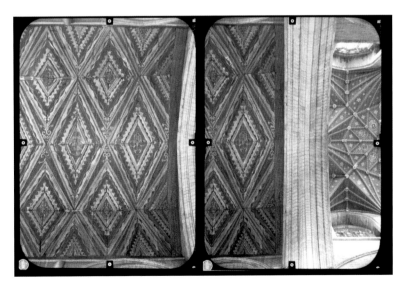

A photogrammetric plot of
four of the 13th-century
ceiling panels. The plot
contains ferramenta and
painted detail.

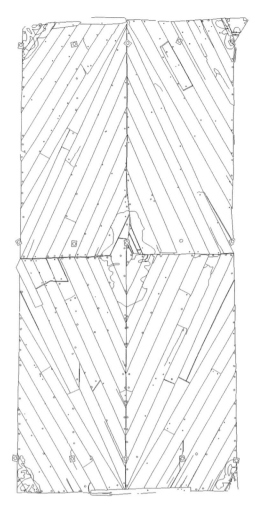

100mm lens in order to cover the two canted side sections of the ceiling, but in the end this was not required owing to the excellent coverage provided by the ground-based photographs.

5.5.3 Photogrammetry

The initial requirement of the project was a set of photogrammetric line drawings (Fig 56). These were to be plotted on A1+ sheets at a scale of 1:20 and were to cover the architectural detail within the first 7m of ceiling at the eastern end of the nave – which was to be the extent of the first phase of conservation works. In addition, a set of A3-format drawings at the larger scale of 1:10 were needed during the actual conservation works on site to enable all the visible structural features such as nail heads, screw threads and tie bolts, as well as the painted detail itself, to be referenced.

In discussion with the conservation consultant and architect, the precise level of detail for the survey was agreed. All of the detail was recorded according to the English Heritage standard specification, although the CAD layering convention was reduced down to three layers – boards, fixings and painting. During this initial plotting work some interesting problems arose.

The first was how best to represent each of the oak boards that made up the actual ceiling. As each board overlapped its neighbour it was impossible to record accurately all four sides, as one side was usually hidden from view. It was therefore decided that where part of a board was hidden by the overlap of another, the visible edges only would be plotted as an unclosed three-dimensional polyline.

Secondly, as some of the painted detail was difficult to interpret successfully as a line, particularly when viewed at high magnification, it was decided to plot this detail as a basic outline only and to infill this outline with a scaled photographic image.

Using this initial plotting work as a benchmark, an accurate estimate was provided

to the architect of the cost involved in photogrammetrically processing the remaining 55m of ceiling to the same level of detail, using the stereo-photographs and survey control data provided by the English Heritage Metric Survey Team. This information was used by the Dean and Chapter to procure the rest of the plotting work.

5.5.4 The use of orthophotography

As noted above, little of the painted detail was to be recorded as line work. Instead, a scaled photographic image was to be utilised and it is here that the application of digital

The orthophotograph of the
entire nave ceiling.

photogrammetric techniques, in particular the orthophotograph, was to become crucial to the documentation of the project.

The colour negatives were scanned at 22.5-micron resolution, using a photogrammetric scanner, producing files of approximately 120 MB each. These were imported into a Helava digital photogrammetric workstation, running SOCET Set software, and processed to form a digital orthophotograph of the ceiling at 5mm pixel resolution with a file size of 90 MB (Fig 57).

The major difficulty encountered during this project was the colour balancing of the twenty-three colour images used during the production of the orthophotograph. Even though geometrically correct scans were utilised, the slight variations in exposure within each colour negative caused by the use of natural light appeared to have upset the automated scanning process usually employed during the scanning of aerial imagery. This resulted in individual scans that were incorrectly colour balanced and that, when joined together, produced a very fluctuating colour image even after processing with Adobe PhotoShop®. Eventually the photographs were re-scanned using Kodak Photo-CD in an attempt to produce colour images that could be evenly joined together.

Extracts from the complete orthophotograph were provided in digital form for the conservators working on the scaffolded ceiling.

These images were imported into Corel-DRAW running on laptop computers to provide a backdrop to the line drawings, which were converted from the DXF format. The conservators annotated the drawings while on site (Fig 58).

5.5.5 REDM survey

During the conservation work the team needed to match detail from below the ceiling to the roof structure above. The roof structure consisted of 19th-century timber trusses holding up the original medieval timbers. Because of the inaccessible nature of the roof space (Fig 59) and since there was no clear field of sight for image-based survey, an REDM survey with real-time CAD mapping was undertaken.

Every bolt, timber fixing, beam, etc of the roof had to be recorded. The majority of the data was gathered using an REDM theodolite, which fed information directly into CAD via the TheoLT software programme. When the matt dark timber in the near-dark environment caused a weak return of the laser beam, detail points were captured using a prism on a pole of known height. When detail was still inaccessible hand measurements were taken and fed directly into the CAD drawing.

Roof structures present particular problems to surveyors because of difficulties of access and limited space. Hand survey and

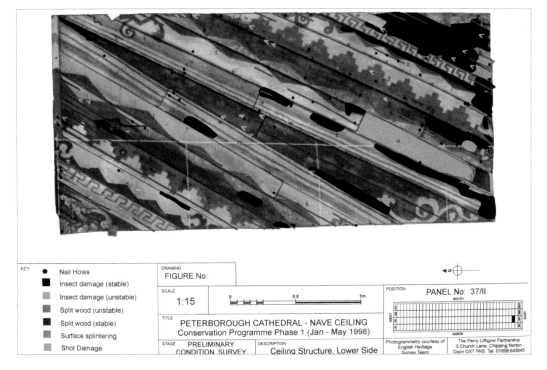

KEY
- Nail Holes
- Insect damage (stable)
- Insect damage (unstable)
- Split wood (unstable)
- Split wood (stable)
- Surface splintering
- Shot Damage

DRAWING FIGURE No:

SCALE 1:15   0   0.5   1m

TITLE PETERBOROUGH CATHEDRAL - NAVE CEILING
Conservation Programme Phase 1 (Jan - May 1998)

STAGE PRELIMINARY CONDITION SURVEY

DESCRIPTION Ceiling Structure, Lower Side

POSITION PANEL No: 37/II
SOUTH
WEST
NORTH
EAST

Photogrammetry courtesy of English Heritage Survey Team

The Perry Lithgow Partnership
5 Church Lane, Chipping Norton
Oxon OX7 5NS Tel. 01608 643645

Figure 58
A plot of part of the orthophotograph overlaid with the photogrammetric line drawing and subsequently annotated by the conservators. Using the orthophotograph and the line drawing, the conservators were able to work from an image of the ceiling as well as the outline physical structure of the boards.
[© The Perry Lithgow Partnership]

Figure 59
View of the cathedral roof
showing some of the
obstacles to undertaking the
metric survey.

5.5.6 Benefits of techniques deployed

The size of the ceiling and the inherent difficulties of access meant that an image-based survey method was the safest and most economical solution. The three-dimensional nature of the surface of the ceiling precluded the use of rectified photography, narrowing the choice to either photogrammetry or orthophotography. In the end the requirement for both the delineation of the boards and fixings and the depiction of the paintings meant that a combination of photogrammetry and orthophotography was required.

REDM combined with hand survey has proved an economical survey technique where metric survey is required in areas that are confined, difficult to access and have limited line of sight. As such, it was the only technique considered for surveying the roof. The use of real-time CAD helped the surveyors in three ways. First, it was immediately apparent if spurious points had been recorded. Secondly, having the recorded data as a CAD drawing gave the surveyor a visual reference of what had been surveyed and what data still needed to be captured. Finally, measurements taken by hand could

REDM can help overcome these, but the lack of a line of sight meant that spur stations had to be set out from the existing traverse to capture obscured roof data (Fig 60). The roof drawing was completed in the office in Auto-CAD and individual elements were separated into groups to inform the understanding of the structure.

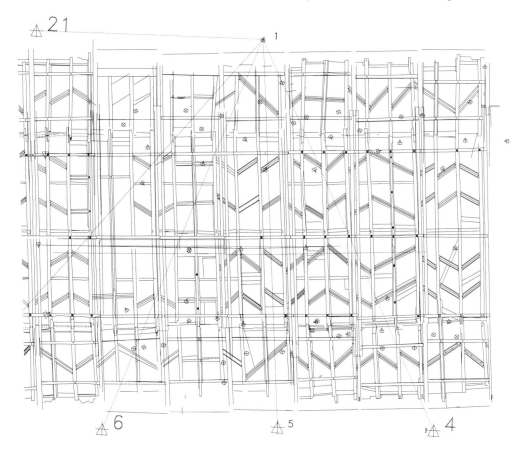

Figure 60
Part of the REDM and
hand survey of the dark
side of the ceiling. The red
lines indicate the complex
control network that was
required because the lines of
sight were obscured by
obstacles (see Fig 59).

be entered directly into the CAD drawing, saving on time spent digitising in the office.

The need to survey the ceiling and its supporting roof structure required the adoption of several surveying techniques. The use of a single control system and CAD as the digital integration platform ensured that all the survey products could be combined and positioned in a local three-dimensional coordinate system. This made it possible to produce two-dimensional plots that combined photogrammetry showing the roof structure with orthophotography showing the related ceiling structure, thus enabling the conservators to fix the painted boards from the flat side of the ceiling through to the roof structure above (Fig 61). Without the survey drawings this would have been extremely difficult.

5.6 Whitby Abbey headland

Whitby Abbey and the headland overlook the town of Whitby in North Yorkshire. The abbey was originally founded in AD 657 and is famous as the site of the Synod of Whitby, when the Northumbrian church aligned itself with Rome rather than the Celtic church. The present abbey church was built on the site of the original and its earliest parts date from the 11th century. Also on the headland are St Mary's church and the shell of the banqueting house, which dates from 1672 (Fig 62).

The range of buildings on the headland site – from the ruins of the abbey to the complex structure of St Mary's church – has required the use of a wide variety of survey methods. These have included techniques with a long pedigree for recording architecture (such as hand survey and photogrammetry), traditional land-survey methods and aerial photography to produce topographic plans. The ability to produce orthophotographs and to construct three-dimensional models meant that new methods for the presentation of survey data could be explored.

5.6.1 Photogrammetry of the abbey church

The English Heritage Metric Survey Team was originally involved in producing photogrammetric line drawings of the elevations of the abbey church in a number of phases throughout the 1990s. Stereo-photography was acquired during several sorties using a combination of metric and semi-metric cameras (see Fig 10). A Rollei 6006 120 format with a 50mm lens was used for areas with restricted access. A Wild P31 5in. × 4in. format with 100mm lens was used for the majority of shots while a Zeiss UMK 30/1318 5in. × 7in. format with 300mm lens was used for the highest elevations so that the stand-off distance could be increased and vertical tilt thus reduced.

The control took the form of plastic targets, or detail points where necessary, which were coordinated by theodolite intersection. A network of permanent survey stations was established within the grounds of the abbey to which all control points were related.

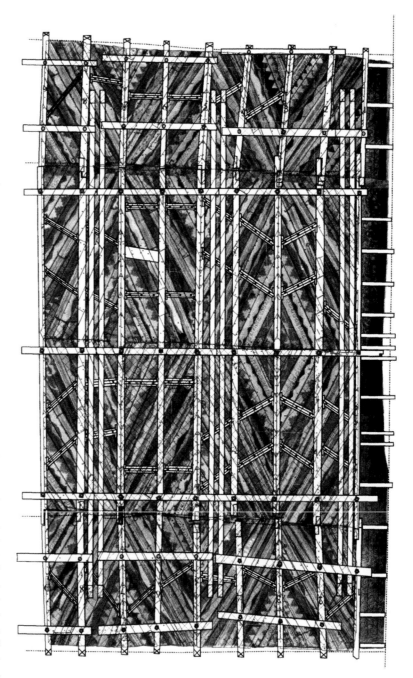

Figure 61

The ceiling superstructure was overlaid with the orthophotograph to allow the conservators to match detail from the ceiling to the roof structure above. [© The Perry Lithgow Partnership]

Figure 62 (above, left)
View of Whitby headland
from the new town. St
Mary's church is to the left,
the remains of the abbey
church can be seen to the
right of St Mary's and the
banqueting house is to the
right of the red-roofed
youth hostel.

Figure 63 (above, right)
A reconstruction of the east
face of Whitby Abbey
church.

Figure 64
(facing page, top)
Aerial stereo-photography
of Whitby headland. St
Mary's church can be seen
to the bottom left of the left-
hand photograph.

Elevation drawings were produced using a Kern DSR 14 stereo-plotter recording directly into a CAD system. Plots at 1:20 scale were produced (*see* Fig 12); these were passed to a consultant archaeologist who, working from scaffolding, annotated the drawings with any corrections and details of lithology, tooling and weathering. Final drawings showing phasing and a conjectural as-built design were produced (Fig 63).

5.6.2 The headland project

During the 1990s English Heritage widened its interest to include the whole of the Whitby Abbey headland. This included mapping the entire area using aerial photography (Fig 64). The aerial stereo-pairs were scanned and used to produce a topographic survey and an orthophotograph. If required, these products can be combined as one image (Fig 65). The controlled scanned photography was also used to generate a

DTM of the headland, which, when draped with the orthphotograph, enabled a three-dimensional fly-around to be produced (Fig 66).

A consequence of the aerial survey and the desire to survey all the historic buildings on the headland was the need for a common coordinate system. A larger network of permanent survey stations was established using GPS. All the survey stations, including the original ones within the abbey grounds, were related to the OSNG.

5.6.3 St Mary's church

St Mary's church was established in the 12th century and has been altered throughout its lifetime, particularly in the Georgian era. It has a distinctive interior, with a large number of gallery and box pews dating from the late 17th to late 18th centuries, and a number of interesting and unusual wall monuments.

It was decided that several methods were needed to survey the church. The interior was surveyed using a combination of photogrammetry, rectified photography and measured drawing. Photogrammetry was used for the chancel, which is now of standard bare ashlar construction. All the elevations of the nave, including the box and gallery pews, were recorded using rectified photography and dimensioned sketches. The photography and

hand drawing were controlled using an REDM wire-frame. The wire-frame was constructed on site using real-time CAD on a field computer. A long sectional elevation was produced illustrating the chancel and the complex arrangement of the nave (Fig 67). A stereo-photography and control package of the exterior elevations was also acquired and archived as an ante-disaster measure.

5.6.4 The banqueting house and courtyard

The banqueting house (Fig 68) was built between 1672 and 1682 and has been a shell since its roof was blown off in the mid-18th century. In the late 1990s plans were formulated to insert a modern visitor centre into this shell. In order to design the visitor centre

Figure 65 (below)
A topographic survey and an orthophotograph can be obtained from controlled stereo-pairs. Here, both products were assembled and combined using a digital photogrammetric workstation.

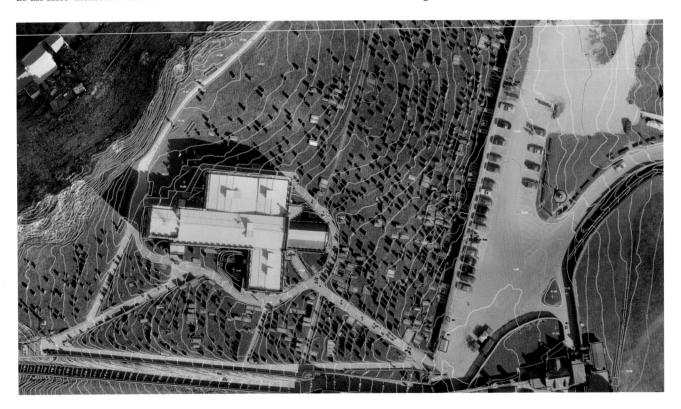

Figure 66
A low-resolution screen shot of the three-dimensional fly-around produced from the controlled aerial photography of the headland. The stereo-pair of Whitby headland was used to produce a DTM, which was then draped with the orthophotographic image.

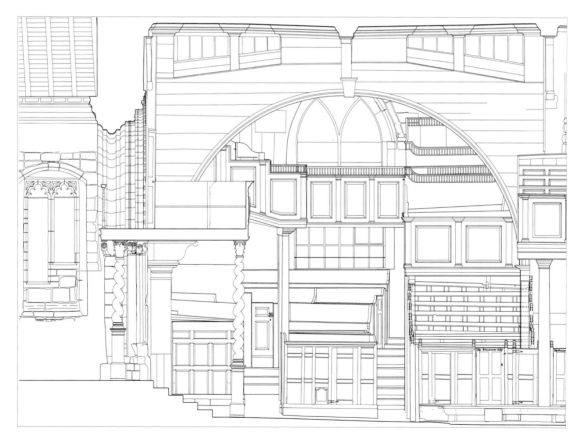

Figure 67
Part of the complex sectional elevation of St Mary's church, Whitby. This drawing was produced using a combination of survey techniques, all referenced to a common control. An REDM wire-frame was used to control hand-survey and rectified photographic data in the main body of the church and part of the chancel was covered using photogrammetry.

accurate three-dimensional drawings of the existing structure were required. These were produced using photogrammetric methods (Fig 69), with particular attention being paid to the three-dimensional integrity of the plotting. The architect and engineer were supplied with both plots and the CAD files.

An investigative archaeological excavation was undertaken as part of the planning process for the new visitor centre. This revealed an extensive decorative cobbled courtyard, which dated from the 17th century and measured 60m × 30m. The usual archaeological practice of hand drawing the revealed surface using a 1m × 1m frame was deemed impracticable for an area this size and it was therefore decided to record the courtyard using rectified photography. In order to reduce the number of photographs required, oblique photography and digital rectification were employed (Fig 70), but even so in excess of 200 photographs were taken. The digitally rectified photographs were montaged together to produce an overall

Figure 68
The banqueting house prior to its reuse as the English Heritage visitor centre.

Figure 69
Part of the photogrammetric plot of the banqueting house.

55

*Figure 70 (near right)
Lack of time and of
vertical access meant that
only oblique photographs
could be taken of the
courtyard floor. These were
later rectified digitally.*

*Figure 71 (far right)
Part of the courtyard floor
digitally rectified and
montaged.*

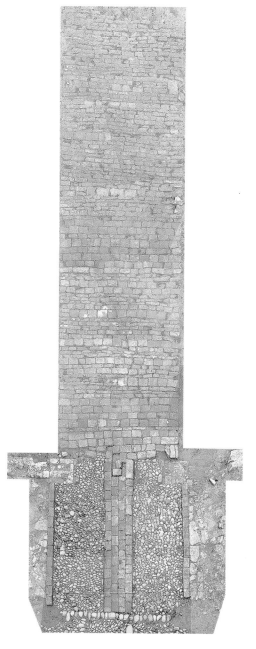

scaled metric survey of the floor, part of
which can be seen in Figure 71.

Another option would have been to bring
in a hydraulic lift, but as the only access to
the courtyard at the time was through an
archway, the size of the lift was limited, making it difficult to cover the whole of the area.
In order to maintain accuracy across the
entire courtyard coordinate controlled targets were used. These were surveyed using
bearing and distance observations to a mini-
prism held directly on to each target. The
advent of co-axial REDM means that this
aspect of the project could have been carried
out more quickly, but the drawback of this is
that the accuracy of REDM significantly
reduces with shallow angles of incidence.

5.6.5 Control

The many different survey techniques
employed on the headland all have one thing
in common – the site grid. In an ideal world
the grid for the whole of the headland would
have been established before any work was
carried out. As it was, however, the drawings of the abbey church had to be trans-
formed into the new system established
by GPS.

6
Conclusion

Metric survey has the potential to communicate the complexities of our historic environment, but it can only do so when it is combined with the surveyor's skills in observation and high standards in the art of drawing. The surveyor's understanding of the subject, usually acquired through close contact, often determines the effectiveness of the output.

6.1 Base-level metric survey for ante-disaster recovery

Metric survey can deliver reliable data in the event of fabric damage or loss. Surveys for ante-disaster recovery need to use archive photography combined with a supporting precise minimum measurement set. Simple stereo-photography can achieve this, with modest equipment and basic metric control.

The following are essential for base-level metric survey photography:

- the presence of a scale bar in the photograph
- overlapping coverage of the subject
- the location of the photographs on a sketch plan
- the use of a camera of known metric performance.

Historic structures are three-dimensional and photography has the potential to enable three-dimensional data recovery. Much valuable three-dimensional information is contained in photography and the means to extract it are improving as digital methods evolve. It is important to consider how the photographic survey will be used for data recovery as simple precautions (such as stereo-photography) can maximise the metric performance of imagery.

6.2 Appropriate methods and practice

In order to choose which methods are most appropriate for a particular survey, it is important to recognise both the potential and the limitations of each technique. The suitability of a technique is determined not only by the size, complexity and type of structure to be surveyed but also by the purpose of the survey. The level of precision required will also be determined by consideration of these factors.

No single survey process is likely to provide a complete record of a building. The need to deploy a combination of techniques should be recognised at an early stage, preferably before briefs or budgets are finalised. The use of complementary techniques requires careful planning to ensure that a suitable system of survey control is established and that each area of the site is assessed for the most appropriate survey method.

The following principles underpin good practice in the survey of historic buildings:

- time spent on reconnaissance is seldom wasted
- work 'from the whole to part', ie from control (whole) down to the architectural detail (part)
- match the method to the desired product and available resources
- never expect more from survey data than the method deployed can deliver
- anticipate the end-user's requirements
- agree a common CAD format at the beginning of the project
- use photographs with some measurement or control to supplement the drawn survey.

A useful guide to the products a project manager can expect from each survey technique can be found in sample specifications produced by the English Heritage Metric Survey Team. In addition *The Presentation of Historic Building Survey in CAD* (English Heritage 1999) sets out systems of organising survey data as well as quality standards for products. Further advice can be sought from English Heritage's Metric Survey Team, Historical Analysis and Research Team, Centre for Archaeology and Architectural Investigation unit (Tel: English Heritage switchboard 020 7973 3000).

57

Appendix 1
Metric survey project brief

Project brief checklist

The project brief sets out the requirements of the survey. The following is a general checklist of the factors that need to be covered, although these will vary according to the nature of a particular project. Other site-specific variables will also need to be included on an individual brief as appropriate.

- Site-related information – location, access, site visits, health and safety factors, clearance of vegetation
- Required liaison with other appointed contractors (eg archaeologists)
- Standard specification for the survey type(s)
- Required accuracy and height data for survey control
- Required orientation of the survey grid
- Temporary targets and their removal
- Artificial illumination
- Use of minor control generated by triangulation
- Completeness – variation in level of detail recorded and/or additional measurement required
- Variation in the rate and/or mode of recording photogrammetric data
- Variation in or required phasing of processing
- Use of film-based imagery with a negative scale different from the standard specification
- Use of monochrome and/or colour imagery
- Specification of any required scaling techniques
- Specific digital format for presentation and storage medium
- Variation on standard CAD layering or file-naming conventions
- The desired scale of hard-copy output
- Areas to be provided as initial samples
- Presentation of circular features (eg the un-peeling of circular towers and their presentation as a flat wall)
- Specific information required on each photograph (eg photographic labels)
- Number and detail of data sets provided and delivery details
- The precise format and file type of the archive to be held by contractors

- Conditions under which liquidated liabilities apply

An example project brief

This example project brief is the one used by The English Heritage Metric Survey Team for the Rectified Photography and Plans of the Powder Magazines, Tilbury Fort, Essex.

General Details
Rectified photography of the exterior and interior elevations of the Powder Magazines and their associated blast walls is required prior to a programme of consolidation. Plans of the interiors are also required.

Location
Address: Tilbury Fort, Tilbury, Essex, RM18 7NR
Directions: The Fort is signed from Tilbury town centre.
National Grid Reference: TQ 651754

Access
The site is open to the public from 10.00 to 16.00 Wednesday to Sunday in winter except 24–26 December and 1 January. Access to the site for purposes of estimating and carrying out the work must be arranged in advance by contacting the Head Custodian. Work outside public opening days/hours may be possible and should be arranged through David Andrews.

Site Visits/Meetings
The contractor is strongly recommended to inspect the site before estimating for the project.

Health & Safety
See Clause 25 of Schedule 4: Conditions of a Framework Agreement for the Provision of Metric Survey Services.

Copyright
English Heritage will retain all copyright as per Clause 14 of Schedule 4: Conditions of a Framework Agreement for the Provision of Metric Survey Services.

Construction (Design & Management) Regulations
The Construction (Design & Management) Regulations 1994 are to be applied to this project. This means, among other things, that all electrical equipment used on site must have an up-to-date Portable Appliance Test (PAT) certificate.

Risk Assessment
The consultants are to provide a written risk assessment before work commences on site. Particular note should be made of the risks of using electrical equipment and access equipment.

Site Clearance
The exterior elevations of one of the Magazines are obscured by vegetation which will be cleared prior to survey work commencing. The other Magazine is clear of obstruction. The interior of one of the Magazines contains an exhibition consisting of display boards which cannot be removed. The other contains a number of historical artefacts, which will be removed prior to work commencing.

Completeness of Survey
All the elevations marked in blue are to be photographed and mosaiced. The elevations marked in yellow are to be covered by single-scaled images.

Use of Temporary Targets
See Section 2.3.11 of the Rectified Photographic Survey Specification and Section 2.5 of the General Specification.

Use of Artificial Illumination
It will be necessary to use artificial illumination in order to undertake this project.

Provision of Temporary Notice of Survey
A notice bearing the following text is to be supplied by the contractors and displayed where they are working:
Contractors' name are working in this area to produce a rectified photographic survey prior to a programme of repairs. We apologise for any inconvenience this may cause.

Proposed Timetable
Please insert a proposed delivery timetable bearing in mind that the survey is required as soon as possible.

Area of survey

Mosaiced rectified photography is required of the following areas marked in blue on the plan.

- The exterior elevations of the Magazines, including the side faces of the buttresses.
- Both faces of the blast wall.
- Single-scaled distance rectified photographs are required to provide coverage of all the interior elevations as marked in yellow on the plan.
- Full detail plans are required of each of the Magazines excluding the blast walls.

Notes to be Read in Conjunction with Rectified Photography Survey Specification

Please read the following in conjunction with the specification. The section numbers below refer to those in the specification. The lack of a note to a particular section should not be taken to mean that the section does not apply.

2.1.3 Monochrome/colour

Colour photography is required for the exterior mosaics while monochrome is to be used for the interior single images.

2.1.6 The use of small format image platforms

The use of negatives of less than 60mm × 60mm will not be acceptable.

2.2.5 Use of oblique imagery

The use of oblique imagery will be required due to the proximity of the blast wall to the main elevations and the requirement to cover the side faces of the buttresses. The tilts should be kept to the minimum necessary to achieve complete coverage.

2.3.2 Scaled rectified imagery

The interior single images are to be controlled by scaled distance, whether this is achieved through the use of a scale bar or taped distances between targets, is at the contractors' discretion.

2.3.3 Controlled rectified imagery

The mosaiced exterior photography is to be controlled by coordinated targets. The curved section of the south west corner of the blast wall is to be split into vertical sections with a chord of approximately one metre and presented as a number of vertical strips.

2.3.6 Site grid

There is an existing site grid. Details of nearby permanent stations and their coordinates will be supplied to the contractor.

2.3.7 Local grids

If none of the existing survey stations can be relocated, a new grid is to be established as described in the specification.

2.3.9 Vertical datum

Any new grid is to be levelled to two nearby Ordnance Survey Bench Marks.

2.4.3 Scale of output

The photomosaics and single images are to be printed at 1:50 scale.

2.4.4 Areas for processing

All those areas marked in blue on the plan are to be presented as photomosaics. All those areas marked in yellow are to be processed as single-scaled images.

2.4.6 Provision of digital data

The mosaiced images are to be supplied in TIFF format and referenced to the coordinate system in AutoCAD R14 files.

2.4.7 Image filenames

The AutoCAD files and associated image files should be named as per the specification. The standard abbreviation for Tilbury Fort is TIL. The files should be numbered beginning with 01.

2.6.5 Acceptable output

The photomosaics are to be plotted in colour onto semi-gloss or gloss paper.

2.7.1 Sample image

Please supply at least one sample rectified print for the interior before proceeding with the rest of the printing.

2.7.2 Preliminary hard copy plots

Please supply at least one sheet plotted on semi-gloss/gloss paper with the preliminary plots.

2.8.1 Labelling

The control prints and the negative sleeves are to be labelled as per the specification.

2.8.2 Labelling information

Monument Name	Tilbury Fort – Powder Magazines
Monument No	xxxx
Survey No	00/135/1R
Item No	Each photograph must be given a unique number.
Camera Type	Insert the make and model of the camera used.
Survey Date	Month and year survey was carried out.

2.8.8 Provision of materials

To be supplied to English Heritage, Metric Survey Team, 37 Tanner Row, York, YO1 6WP:

1 × set of plots of the photomosaics on gloss/semi-gloss paper
1 × set of the scaled rectified prints
1 × set of digital data on CD-ROM
All other deliverables as described in the specification

To be supplied to English Heritage, 44 Derngate, Northampton, NN1 1UH

1 × set of plots of the photomosaics on gloss/semi-gloss paper
1 × set of the scaled rectified prints
1 × set of digital data on CD-ROM

Notes to be Read in Conjunction with Specification for Architectural Survey

3.1 Survey is to be supplied in the form of:
- Plans

3.4 Level of detail
3.4.2 1:50 scale detail is to be supplied.
3.7 A dashed line is to be used to depict overhead detail.

4.0 Control of survey
4.1 See Sections 2.3.6, 2.3.7 and 2.3.9 above.

7.1 Drawing file format
The data is to be supplied in AutoCAD R14 .DWG files.

Provision of materials

To be supplied to English Heritage, Metric Survey Team, 37 Tanner Row, York, YO1 6WP:

1 × set of plots on paper before the delivery of the rest of the data
1 × set of plots on stable polyester draughting film
1 × set of digital data on CD-ROM

To be supplied to English Heritage, 44 Derngate, Northampton, NN1 1UH:

1 × set of plots on stable polyester draughting film
1 × set of digital data CD-ROM

Appendix 2
Glossary

Boolean operations The form of mathematical logic used to produce solid models in AutoCAD

Cavetto A simple concave moulding

Cimatium The crowning member of a cornice, generally in the form of a double curved moulding (cyma)

Coordinates Cartesian description of a position, usually a grid reference

Datum line A horizontal level line used as a reference for an entire drawing. Other level lines can be referenced to the datum line

Detail points Specified points in the fabric that can be used for control if the historic fabric is inaccessible or too delicate for stuck-on targets

Digital model A model that is constructed on a computer using specific software. These models can be viewed and printed from any angle and used to set up animation sequences

Digitising The process of converting hard-copy line drawings or photographs into digital data

DXF format Drawing eXchange format. An AutoCAD file type for importing or exporting drawings to or from AutoCAD

Ferramenta Small ironwork found in buildings

Formal adjustments An accepted form of error distribution (eg a Bowditch correction applied to a traverse)

Hot shoe spirit bubble A spirit level that is placed in the hot shoe of a camera

Inspector of Ancient Monuments The English Heritage officer with responsibility for ancient monuments, able to offer help and advice

Isometric sketches An explanatory diagram in which the verticals are true, with horizontal axes displayed at 60 and 30 degrees to each other

Laser plummet A vertical level line created by a laser, used for setting up surveying instruments over a specific point

Laser scanning Collecting a three-dimensional data-cloud with an automated laser-modulated infra-red distance measurement system

Level line Use of a string, chalk or laser line to define a level from which measurements can be taken

Mutules One of a series of projecting inclined blocks of a Doric cornice

Passing tolerances The clearance required to allow parts to fit

Plumb line A vertical level line created by using a plumb bob, often used during hand surveys

Precise A measurement can be said to be precise if it can be repeated to a known tolerance (eg a distance of 5m measured with a level of precision to ±10mm)

Ruggedised computer A computer that can be used in the field, exposed to the elements

Scale tolerance The degree to which a drawing at a particular scale can be enlarged and still remain precise. For example, the survey of a plan intended for plotting at 1:500 scale is unlikely to be sufficiently precise to allow useful plotting at 1:50

Scheduled Monument Consent Consent for works to a scheduled monument granted by the Secretary of State on the advice of English Heritage

Station A known point with arbitrary or OSNG coordinates from which points of detail can be recorded

Thematic observation The subjective values used to analyse and so understand the data provided by metric survey

Three-dimensional digitising A component of real-time mapping techniques, three-dimensional digitising refers to the positioning of field data in CAD using spatial references, ie using their three-dimensional coordinate values

Three-dimensional polyline An AutoCAD line format, used for drawing three-dimensional objects

Topographic survey The controlled measurement of natural and artificial landscape features presented in plan or as a three-dimensional data set reading as a plan

Tribrach An interchangeable base plate for theodolite and targets that sits on a tripod

UCS User Coordinate System. An Auto-CAD concept, the UCS makes it possible for the CAD operator to orientate objects and views to a defined set of drawing coordinates

Wire-frame A CAD line drawing of a historic building, or part of one, that is used to control the input of further detailed survey data. For example, part of a photogrammetric survey, or an instrument survey, can provide the wire-frame to control hand-survey data

Witness diagram A diagram with measurements, which describes the position of control stations so they can be found and reoccupied if needed

Appendix 3

References and further reading

Alcock, N W *et al* 1996. *Recording Timber-Framed Buildings: An Illustrated Glossary.* (Council for British Archaeology Practical Handbooks in Archaeology 5). (2nd edn; Council for British Archaeology)

Andrews, D *et al* 1995. *The Survey and Recording of Historic Buildings and Monuments.* (Association of Archaeological Illustrators and Surveyors Technical Paper No. 12)

Balanzi, M *et al* 2001. 'A terrestrial 3D Laser Scanner: Accuracy tests' in CIPA *Proceedings of CIPA Working Group 6: XVIIIth International Workshop.* (CIPA)

Blake, B and Latimer, M 1999. *Realtime Data Capture for Architectural Survey.* (Proceedings of the Geomatics Division Conference, RICS)

Bowden, M (ed) 1999. *Unravelling the Landscape: An Inquisitive Approach to Archaeology.* (Tempus)

Brunskill, R W 2000. *Vernacular Architecture: An Illustrated Handbook.* (4th edn; Faber and Faber)

Buchanan, T 1983. *Photographing Historic Buildings for the Record.* (HMSO)

Chitham, R 1980. *Measured Drawing for Architects.* (The Architectural Press)

CIPA 2002. *Proceedings of the CIPA Working Group 6 International Workshop on 'Scanning for Cultural Heritage Recording – Complementing or Replacing Photogrammetry'.* (Ziti Publishing)

Clark, K 2001. *Informed Conservation* (2nd edn, 2003; English Heritage)

Cossons, N and Trinder, B 1979. *The Iron Bridge: Symbol of the Industrial Revolution.* (Ironbridge Gorge Museum Trust/Moonraker Press)

Digges, Leonard and Digges, Thomas 1571. *Pantometria.* (Henrie Bynneman)

English Heritage 1999. *The Presentation of Historic Building Survey in CAD.* (English Heritage)

English Heritage 2000 *Metric Survey Specifications for English Heritage.* (2nd edn, 2003; English Heritage)

English Heritage 2002. *With Alidade and Tape: Graphical and Plane Table Survey of Archaeological Earthworks.* (English Heritage)

English Heritage 2003. *Where on Earth Are We? The Role of Global Positioning System (GPS) in Archeological Field Survey.* (English Heritage)

de Haan, D 2000. *The Iron Bridge, Historic Building Survey, Record and Analysis* (The Ironbridge Institute)

Hare, J N 1985. *Battle Abbey: The Eastern Range and the Excavations of 1978–80.* (HBMCE Archaeological Report 2)

ICOMOS 1990. *Guide to Recording Historic Buildings.* (Butterworth Architecture)

Ionides, J 1999. *Thomas Farnolls Pritchard of Shrewsbury: Architect and 'Inventor of Cast-Iron Bridges'.* (Dog Rose Press)

Palladio, Andrea 1570. *The Four Books of Architecture.* (Dover 1965)

Reekie, F 1946. *Draughtmanship: Architectural and Building Graphics.* (repr 1982; Edward Arnold)

Serlio, Sebastiano 1611. *The Five Books of Architecture* (repr of English edn of 1611)

Ware, Isaac 1756–7. *A Complete Body of Architecture.*

Appendix 4

Information sources

Ancient Monuments Society
St Ann's Vestry Hall
2 Church Entry
London EC4V 5HB
020 7236 3934
www.ancientmonumentssociety.org.uk

Association of Local Government
Archaeological Officers (ALGAO)
01287 205863
algao.cji@ntlworld.com
www.algao.org.uk

The Brooking Collection
University of Greenwich
Oakfield Lane
Dartford
Kent DA1 2SZ
020 8331 9897

CIPA (the ICOMOS/ISPRS Committee
for Documentation of Cultural Heritage)
Paul Bryan (UK contact)
The Metric Survey Team
English Heritage
37 Tanner Row
York YO1 6WP
http://cipa.icomos.org

Council for British Archaeology (CBA)
Bowes Morrell House
111 Walmgate
York YO1 9WA
01904 671417
www.britarch.ac.uk

Department for Culture, Media and
Sport
www.culture.gov.uk

English Heritage
23 Savile Row
London W1S 2ET
020 7973 3000
www.english-heritage.org.uk

English Heritage Regions
North East   0191 261 1585
North West   0161 242 1400
Yorkshire   01904 601901
West Midlands   0121 625 6820
East Midlands   01604 735400
East of England   01223 582700
South West   0117 975 0700
South East   01483 252000
London   020 7973 3000

National Monuments Record Centre
(NMRC)
Kemble Drive
Swindon
Wiltshire SN2 2GZ
01793 414600
www.english-heritage.org.uk

English Heritage Postal Sales
c/o Gillards
Trident Works
Temple Cloud
Bristol BS39 5AZ
01761 452966
www.english-heritage.org.uk

European heritage policies and
organisations
www.european-heritage.net

Garden History Society
70 Cowcross Street
London EC1M 6EJ
020 7608 2409
www.gardenhistorysociety.org

Georgian Group
6 Fitzroy Square
London W1T 5DX
020 7529 8920
www.georgiangroup.org.uk

Heritage information
www.heritageinformation.org.uk

Heritage Lottery Fund
7 Holbein Place
London SW1W 8NR
020 7591 6000
www.hlf.org.uk

Historic American Buildings Survey
www.cr.nps.gov/habshaer

Images of England Project
www.imagesofengland.org.uk

Institute of Field Archaeologists
SHES
University of Reading
Whiteknights
PO Box 227
Reading RG6 6AB
0118 931 6446
www.archaeologists.net

Institute of Historic Building
Conservation
www.ihbc.org.uk

International Council on Monuments
and Sites (ICOMOS UK)
10 Barley Mow Passage
London W4 4PH
020 8994 6477
www.icomos.org

Internet sources in architecture and
architectural history
www.library.ucla.edu/libraries/arts/websites/
wwwarch.htm

List of conservation and specialist
organisations
www.buildingconservation.com

National Trust
36 Queen Anne's Gate
London SW1H 9AS
0870 609 5380
www.nationaltrust.org.uk

Public Record Office
www.pro.gov.uk

Royal Institute of British Architects
(RIBA)
66 Portland Place
London W1B 1AD
020 7580 5533
www.riba.org

RIBA Library
www.riba-library.com/oncat

Society of Architectural Historians of
Great Britain
secretary@sahgb.org.uk
www.sahgb.org.uk

Society for the Protection of Ancient
Buildings (SPAB)
37 Spital Square
London E1 6DY
020 7377 1644
www.spab.org.uk

The Stationery Office
www.clicktso.com

The Twentieth Century Society
70 Cowcross Street
London EC1M 6EJ
020 7250 3857
www.c20society.demon.co.uk

United Kingdom Institute for
Conservation
109 The Chandlery
50 Westminster Bridge Road
London SE1 7QY
020 7721 8721
www.ukic.org.uk

Victorian Society
1 Priory Gardens
Bedford Park
London W4 1TT
020 8994 1019
www.victorian-society.org.uk